man
and his
environment:
waste

man and his environment: waste

WESLEY MARX

Harper & Row, Publishers
New York
Evanston
London

**man
and his
environment:
waste**

*Library of Congress Catalog
Card Number:
79-137805*

contents

contents

editors' introduction

The books of the Harper & Row series being published under the general title of *Man and His Environment* are designed to help us understand the world about us, our dependence on it, and what we are doing to it, both good and bad.

From the personal point of view, it has been said that the environment is everything else but me. It is the sky over our heads and the earth beneath our feet. It is other people and any living animal or plant with which we have any connections. It includes what the senses of sight, hearing, taste, smell, and touch tell us about nature. Also, the environment is home, the cities and towns we have built. It includes the landscape that is altered by raising food, feed, and fiber; by the extraction of minerals; by building homes, schools, churches, places of business, and factories, and by building facilities for travel and transport, for the generation of energy, and for communication. The environment includes not only the natural and manmade things about us but also physical and cultural conditions and processes.

All these elements of the environment can be studied, thought about, and worked with individually, but this analytic approach is inadequate for the understanding of the total environment, and it leads to difficulties when we overlook or neglect the consequences of single-purpose actions. This is because the elements of the environment do not occur singly in nature or in culture, but in complex interacting systems. For example, soil is not just decomposed rock. It includes air and water, hundreds of organic and inorganic compounds, and almost innumerable living things, most of which are too small to be seen in a handful of dirt. Water is a simple compound, but we are not likely to encounter it as such. Many substances are dissolved in it, particles are suspended in it, and living creatures float and swim about in it. Everywhere we find mixtures of things, in a drop of pond water, a lump of soil, a breath of air, most things that man makes. Not only do we find mixtures of things everywhere; these things interact with one another because of processes of their own, changing one another and the conditions of the whole.

In this book of the series Wesley Marx has dealt with one important facet of the interrelations between man and his environment. For each of these books, no matter what is the main focus (climate, energy, materials, waste, food, population, recreation, transportation, law, or aesthetics and the cultural roots of our viewpoints), we have asked the authors to take a holistic point of view and to write about interconnections, interactions, consequences, and, in fact, the systems of man and nature together. As broad-gauged thinkers and scientists, they are well equipped for this demanding goal.

Man has become the leading cause of environmental change. He is discovering that he is responsible for much that he does not like—air and water pollution, poisons in our food, deteriorated cities— and that in order to correct such disagreeable, unhealthy, and unpleasant conditions he must understand the ecology of his environmental interrelations.

Although this book can stand alone, it is also an integral part of the series on *Man and His Environment*.

John E. Bardach
Marston Bates
Stanley A. Cain

preface

I would like to express my appreciation to Marston Bates for inviting me to participate in the Man and His Environment Series and write on wastes. In writing a book on ocean conservation, I came to learn that even the condition of the open sea can be influenced by waste management or the lack of it. In reading the entire manuscript, Dr. John Bardach made very helpful suggestions and encouraged me to expand on the broad significance of the waste challenge in the last chapter. Dr. Bardach also helped protect me from some of my copy errors.

Ed Hauser and Gale Ruffin, manager and chief engineer, respectively, of the Santee County Water District, and Ray Stoyer, director of planning for the Irvine Ranch Water District, were most helpful in informing me about water reclamation and its potential in waste management. Mr. David Evans of the Colorado School of Mines provided pertinent information about the hazards of deep-well disposal while Mr. Wilfred Shields of the Maryland Department of Health forwarded helpful material on restoration of derelict mining land with sanitary landfill. Mr. Thomas O'Brien of the Orange County, California, Road Department's landfill operation was also helpful. Mr. Evans and Mr. Stoyer reviewed and corrected relevant portions of the manuscript. However, the final responsibility remains the author's.

In doing much of my literature research, I relied on the book and periodical collections at the libraries at the University of California at Irvine and California State College at Fullerton, as well as the Tustin Public Library. The staff at all three libraries were most helpful.

Wesley Marx

1

power without control

The Bible and the classical writers tell us that once there was a race of giants. I've sometimes thought when I looked at the sea through olive terraces I saw it as the giants did. The leaves on the branches might be an old giant's silver eyebrows, bristling over his eyes, the dark trunks would be like his great eyelashes. And beyond would be the blue sea. Such a giant would not smooth back his eyebrows, he would not open his eyes wide, he would want his sight shaded, because in those days the sea must have been brighter than it is today. There were few men then. Millions of men have lived since to pollute the waters with filth. Human beings have produced nothing more persistently and in greater quantities than excrement.

The speaker is Count Diakonov, a King Lear-like figure in *The Birds All Fall Down,* Rebecca West's novel of turn-of-the-century Russian intrigue. Today the pernicious productivity that the Count alludes to haunts our status as the dominant species on this planet and perhaps in the universe. Our excrements, industrial as well as domestic, forever expanding in volume and toxicity, stain our skies as well as our waterways and make natural air and natural water almost gold-rare.

*man
and his
environment:
waste*

Our ability to abuse our environment with our wastes dogs every progressive step we make, as if mocking our own shrewdness. We learn to raise cattle herds in confined feedlots and wind up with mammoth manure piles once dissipated on grazing pastures. We launch exquisite supersonic jets that generate a waste without physical form but with the power to make our eardrums and skyscrapers vibrate—the sonic boom. We create convenient, throw-away aluminum containers only to discover that we may be laying down a new geological deposit of trash. We save millions of lives and billions of dollars of agricultural crops with a cheap chemical compound called DDT, only to learn that DDT residues may be a chemical agent of biological extinction. Our inability to foresee, much less control, our waste-making takes on the form of social regurgitation. As we proudly export our pesticides, our internal combustion engines, our jets, and our other exotic waste-makers to newly developing nations, we tend to infect the globe with this disconcerting habit.

We have showed an awareness of this habit, particularly as it endangers our existence. The mass media are replete with concern about the health hazards and economic damage from water pollution, noise pollution, air pollution, thermal pollution, and pesticide pollution. Waste pollution is becoming a major theme of our artists, composers, and writers. Artists have placed gas masks on representations of the Statue of Liberty to dramatize air pollution while comedians caustically remark, "I like pollution because I can see what I breathe." Tom Lehrer serenades his nightclub audiences with:

*Just go out for a breath of air,
And you'll be ready for Medicare.
The city streets are really quite a thrill,
If the hoods don't get you, the monoxide will.**

Folksinger Pete Seeger builds a sloop called *Clearwater* and sails the Hudson River to mobilize public concern over dirty waters. Arthur Godfrey laments the Santa Barbara oil spill in a ballad.

Recognizing that they must live on this beleaguered planet, high school and college students are becoming increasingly concerned with waste pollution. Students at Massachusetts Institute of Technology and California Institute of Technology have devoted school vacations to racing electric cars across the country in order to help develop a smogless alternative to the internal combustion engine. Students at the University of California at Berkeley clean up San Francisco Bay tidelands used as impromptu dumps. Bay-shore drivers may see on the tidelands a skeletal dinosaur with a toilet-seat head and a wooden-crate body. "Mudflat" or "derelict" art from junk flotsam is also used to dramatize the bay's use as a dump.

Increasing public concern over waste pollution has not escaped state and federal legislators. The various pollutions have qualified for their own special administrations and agencies: the Federal Water Quality Control Agency, the Office of Solid Wastes, the National Aircraft Noise Abatement Council, the National Center for Air Pollution Control.

Despite public concern, artistic outrage, and legislative action, environmental exploitation persists. It persists because special government bureaus and technological fixes cannot, overnight, reverse a habit that, as Count Diakonov observed, is so deeply embedded in human nature. This habit even transcends entirely different political systems. The United States and the Soviet Union share one very common problem—severe waste pollution.

As we try to control our waste-making, we discover just how extensively we use the natural environment as a convenient dump for our waste discharges. As we become aware of the risks and dangers in using our natural life support system as a dump, we learn the limits of our knowledge of this system and our relationship to it. When we try to control our waste discharges, we learn how ineffective our methods of control are. As we attempt to professionalize the profession of waste control, we realize its backwardness. MIT Professor David Wilson observes, "Investigations have shown that in certain areas a disturbingly high proportion of the [refuse collection] industry is under the direct or indirect control of under-world operation. Maintenance of a high quality environment (or, for that matter, a service of maximum value) is not something to which these small businessmen devote a large proportion of their time." In trying to identify a portion of the waste disposal profession accorded good pay, well-appointed facilities, and high standing in the community, one often winds up with the mortician. This status has been achieved less by perfecting an efficient and economical method of disposal then by perfecting elaborate, expensive and land-consuming methods of disposal that pay full heed to human vanity.

In attempting to assess the increasing costs of waste control, we find that traditionally the waste victim, not the waste generator, foots the bill. Our waterways and airsheds have traditionally been considered relatively free goods, in the economic sense, to be exploited at will by anyone—dumpers included. By permitting these limited resources to be used as bottomless dumps, we have actually been subsidizing the degradation of our natural life support system. By trying to create political institutions equal to the scope of waste pollution, we find that a city council is capable of approving waste discharges that may affect the entire continent as well as the oceans.

Amidst all these social encouragements to waste-making, we often find ourselves adapting to waste pollution rather than controlling it. As our affluent wasteloads expand in volume and toxicity, a foreboding question arises: Can we protect ourselves from our wastes? By generating such waste-loads, we are generating industrial power and creature comfort never before seen on this planet and yet, as Paul Sears observes, "But power is not the same thing as control."

SUGGESTED READINGS

At the end of each chapter, suggested readings, including chapter sources, will be listed. Throughout the course, readers will find popular and professional periodicals and government publications of particular value.

power without control

Periodicals especially useful because of their broad approach to waste problems include:

Archives of Environmental Health, American Medical Association, 535 N. Dearborn, Chicago, Ill. Monthly.

American City, Berkshire Common, Pittsfield, Mass. 01201. Monthly. Brief, popular rundowns on new waste control methods.

Audubon, National Audubon Society, 1130 Fifth Ave., New York, N.Y. 10028. Bimonthly.

Bulletin of the Atomic Scientists, Educational Foundation for Nuclear Science, 935 E. 60th St., Chicago, Ill. 60037. Monthly.

Environment, Scientists' Institute for Public Information, 438 N. Skinner, St. Louis, Mo. 63130. Monthly.

Environmental Science and Technology, American Chemical Society, 1155 16th St. N.W., Washington, D.C. 20036. Monthly. Perhaps the single most indispensable source on developments in the waste management field.

Journal of the Sanitary Engineering Division, American Society of Civil Engineers, 345 E. 47th St., New York, N.Y. 10017. Bimonthly.

To relate the book to local and regional questions, the reader can contact state and local agencies, such as sanitation, public health, and air and water quality agencies, for available literature. At the federal level, the following legislative and executive offices can provide helpful material, including publication lists and lists of on-going research and demonstration projects (a presidential proposal to consolidate federal pollution control agencies into an Environmental Protection Agency (EPA) was approved late 1970):

Department of Health, Education, and Welfare—Consumer Protection and Environmental Health Service, which includes Bureau of Solid Waste Management and National Air Pollution Control Administration. HEW is also concerned with health problems raised by noise and radiation emissions.

Department of the Interior—Federal Water Quality Control Administration.

Department of Transportation—Office of Noise Abatement and Federal Aviation Agency.

House Subcommittee on Fisheries and Wildlife Conservation.

House Subcommittee on Science, Research, and Development.

Senate Subcommittee on Air and Water Pollution.

United States Coast Guard. Information on oil pollution.

White House Council of Environmental Quality. Charged with issuing annual reports on the state of the environment.

White House Office of Science and Technology.

Trade and professional associations, particularly in the metal, chemical, and petroleum fields, make available literature relating to their roles in waste questions. For addresses, consult trade and professional directories.

Pollution Abstracts (Box 2369, La Jolla, Calif. 92037) provides bibliographic citations, abstracts, and corresponding indexes on published information concerning pollution and its control. This excellent new source is published six times yearly.

2
man as waste-maker

Waste-free activities are hard to find. Activity itself dissipates energy and matter, thus eating, working, playing, farming, and warring all have one common trait—debris. If we are going to exist as more than sightseers and lovers, we are going to produce wastes. Man is not alone in his waste-making. All life depends on dissipated energy and materials for survival. A blade of grass respires gases into the atmosphere during photosynthesis and provides us with oxygen. Under the warm sun, lakes and oceans release water vapor into the atmosphere to form clouds that irrigate the earth and, in turn, replenish the lakes and the oceans. Frost and wind grind down boulders and release grains of quartz into mountain streams. These grains, ultimately transported to the ocean littoral, accrete on the shore to form 5-mile-long beaches and 200-foot-high sand dunes.

If dead plants and animals remained inert, life would have long since crowded itself off the planet. However, death is integrated into the metabolism of the environment as effectively as respired gases and evaporated water. Dead plants and animals decay and decompose as if they had been outfitted with self-destruct systems. But reconversion, not destruction, is taking place. The forces of decomposition, from vultures to bacteria, break down the autumn leaf, the aging plankton and the dying elephant into life-giving nutrients. The remains of decomposition, humus, fertilizes prairies and jungles. The floor of a redwood forest is literally soundproofed by the accumulated humus of fallen redwoods. Above, a mastlike creaking can be heard. The "masts" are the living redwoods that rise from the humus into the path of sea winds blowing off the Pacific.

Through such decomposition, death is as important as sex in perpetuating life. In this sense, there is no such thing as "waste" in the natural environment. The environment is prepared to dilute, degrade and recycle byproducts of energy and materials dissipation into life processes. The environment is thus dependent on and structured for waste-receiving.

For most of his life, man has lived in harmony and benefited from this ecological ingenuity. The vultures and the bacteria have been equal to the feces and the garbage, the carcasses and the corpses, of a hunter's civilization. Energy conversion at its height was often a matter of throwing another log on the fire. The nomadic nature of the hunter served to disperse his modest wasteload.

As man began to expand his expectations and his range of activities, anti-ecological forces were set in motion. He learned to resist disease and adapt to different environments until he became the most numerous of all large animals and the only worldwide species in existence. Natural controls on man's population size and distribution, which also served to control his waste-making, have been surmounted. In their lifetime, our children may live in a world populated by 15 billion. And man's potential distribution now embraces another "planet," the moon, whose waste-receiving capacity is not yet understood.

In his rise to dominance, man has forsaken nomadism for permanent settlements. This trend serves to concentrate the wasteloads of a population rise out of control. Our children's children may live to see a city with a population of 1 billion.

Living in cities, man has learned to expand his capabilities for energy conversion. Instead of throwing an-

other log on the fire or trapping wind in ship sails, he
has learned to generate energy from coal, oil, and the
atom. He has learned to exploit not only the organic
wealth of the planet but its inorganic wealth: iron, zinc,
copper, and aluminum. He has learned to make his own
synthetic products: plastics, nylon, rayons, and pesticides. To convert raw materials into products, he has developed machines as numerous and diverse as insects,
from sewing machines to nuclear reactors.

This growth in energy and materials conversion generates a wasteload whose diversity, volume, and complex-
ity far exceed a wasteload fueled simply by uncontrolled
population growth and urban concentration. Besides receiving sand grains, autumn leaves, and human excrement, our rivers receive dumped spoil from navigation
projects, hot water from power plants, pesticide runoff
from farms, soap suds from dishwashers, and acid mine
drainage from mines. Besides receiving oxygen from
plants and water vapor from lakes, our atmosphere receives carbon monoxide, lead aerosols, fluorides, hydrocarbons, sulfur dioxide, and sonic booms from smokestacks, auto exhausts, and jet engines. Besides receiving
fallen redwoods, corpses, and prune pits, our land is receiving items that cannot be readily consumed by bacteria or vultures: aluminum cans, junk autos, plastic
cups, copper tailings, and DDT residues.

The tons, cubic yards, and decibels of waste being
generated by energy and materials conversion is now
prodigious by any scale. Each year, the United States
disposes of 7 million autos, 20 million tons of waste
paper, 25 million pounds of toothpaste tubes, 48 billion
cans, and 26 billion bottles and jars. Our waterways receive some 50 trillion gallons of hot water plus unknown
millions of gallons of chemical and organic wastes from
factories, canneries, farms and cities.

Yet this wasteload, however large, promises to grow at
a rate faster than in the past. From throwaway gum
wrappers and paper plates, the "disposable" industry
has expanded into paper ties, dresses, bedsheets, and
jewelry. The pressure to cut maintenance and labor costs
and keep abreast of changing fashion propels the switch
from reusable to one-use items. This "one-use" affluence

adds a new dimension to wasteloads. The average American family uses 850 cans yearly. In one year, for example, consumers of Col. Sanders' Kentucky fried chicken disposed of 22 million foam polystyrene containers, 31 million paperboard buckets, and 110 million regular dinner boxes. Each year, the babies in the United States have their diapers changed some 15.6 billion times. The diapers, being cloth, are generally washed and reused. Now three large corporations are launching a multimillion-dollar daytime TV advertising campaign for disposable diapers. Large machines turn wood pulp into 300 disposable diapers per minute. Almost as an afterthought, one corporation has set up a Flushability Task Force to determine just how successfully disposable diapers can be flushed down the toilet.

Through such advances as disposable diapers, each American now produces about 5 pounds of trash each day. The *prorated* amount of solid wastes from industrial and chemical processes raises this figure to 10 pounds per person, according to *Cleaning Our Environment,* a 1969 report by the American Chemical Society. Comedian Milt Kamen recently told how his neighbors became suspicious of him because, as a bachelor non-cook, he had no garbage to put out his front door. Kamen says, "I went to the supermarket and I bought some bachelor garbage—frozen garbage with no defrosting. You just toss it out—chicken bones, coffee grounds, egg shells. I'd get garbage delight—lobster shells, an empty champagne bottle. This impressed my neighbors. They called me 'Mr. Kamen' and they smiled at me and said, 'Drop in to see us, Mr. Kamen—and bring your garbage!' "

Animal wastes, chemical fertilizers, and pesticides now make rural as well as urban areas prime sources of waste. The same carefree attitude toward waste-making pertains. The massive application of insecticides by aerial spraying prompted Dr. Kenneth Boulding to remark, "The response of the insecticide industry to insects is like the response of the United States Air Force to Communists."

Loose mines and rusting barbed wire once characterized the leftover debris of war-making; fallout from nuclear bombs and chemical and biological warfare adds a new dimension to war's waste-making potential.

Traditionally, broad-scale energy and materials conversion has been practiced by a minority of the world's population; the United States uses about 50 percent of the raw-material resources consumed in the world. Our 6 percent of the world's population produces 70 percent of the world's solid wastes. The ambitions of developing nations promise to make intensive energy and materials conversion and its corresponding wasteloads global in nature. Yet this planet is being severely stressed by the wasteloads of just one United States, much less 10, 20, 30 or 100 United Stateses. We often tend to think that having the entire world's 3 billion people live American-style would be heaven on earth, a moral goal worthy of all faiths and persuasions. But from an ecological viewpoint, the wholesale use of DDT in Asia, the universal acceptance of flushable diapers, a worldwide chain of carry-out chicken stands, two cars and a camper trailer in everybody's garage, and the advent of one-use, nonreturnable, nondegradable homes could be disastrous.

The uncontrolled growth of population, cities, and industry creates an ugly anomaly. With the help of Mr. Clean and other commercial folk heroes, we exhibit an unrivaled concern with hygiene. We probably shampoo our hair, deodorize our armpits, and shave our faces with more regularity than any civilization to date. We have, naturally enough, begun to mechanize hygiene: battery-run toothbrushes, electric shavers, washing machines, and dishwashers. Yet aboriginal hunters must rank as cleaner creatures than we, simply because they were unable to dirty their living spaces to the degree we can. While we deodorize our armpits, our wasteloads overcome the waste-receiving capacity of the natural environment in a rather indiscriminate form of chemical and biological warfare.

SUGGESTED READINGS

Hauser, Philip, *The Population Dilemma,* Englewood Cliffs, N.J.: Prentice-Hall, 1963.

Howard, Walter, "The Population Crisis Is Here Now," *Bioscience,* September, 1969.

Landsberg, Hans, *Natural Resources for U.S. Growth,* Baltimore: Johns Hopkins Press, 1964, chaps. 1–3. Published for Resources for the Future.

National Academy of Sciences Committee on Resources and Man, *Resources and Man,* San Francisco: W. H. Freeman & Co., 1969.

Odum, Eugene, *Ecology,* New York: Holt, Rinehart and Winston, 1969.

Shepard, Paul, and Daniel McKinley, eds., *The Subversive Science,* New York: Houghton Mifflin, 1968.

3
the
planet
as dump

When we defecate, spray garden insecticides, or press the auto accelerator, we don't think of ourselves as giving birth to substances formidable enough to alter the sky and the oceans. Products and energy are always being "consumed" in our society, often to the beat of stock-market tickers. Yet if products were truly being consumed in the full sense of the word, books and courses on waste pollution would not be needed. In reality, we are only consuming a product's market value. The remains are considered eligible for release into the environment, and our mundane daily discharges are all capable of leading separate and sometimes extraordinary existences.

The appearance and behavior of liberated wastes is diverse. Some wastes may become highly visible, like junk autos deserted off country roads. Many are colorless, odorless, and invisible to the eye, such as the output of "smokeless" auto exhausts. Some wastes—such as noise—are very noticeable even without tangible physical form.

Wastes can be highly mobile and commute indiscriminately between land, air, and water. DDT residues, for instance, can be found where pest-control programs are virtually unknown—the Arctic. Some wastes have a life measured in minutes or, as in noise, seconds. The lifetime of other wastes, such as DDT and radioactive residues, may be measured in years or decades. Some wastes may be toxic at time of release; other dilute wastes may be concentrated into toxic levels in the flesh of an oyster or the gonads of a pelican by means of a process called biological magnification. If wastes were to remain in their original form, research and courses on waste pollution could be simplified considerably. However, wastes do change form. Photochemical smog is generated by the reaction of various auto fumes "cooking" under sunlight. Through such synergism, harmless wastes may become hazardous.

Being so behaviorally diverse, wastes are difficult to categorize. Wastes may be labeled "soft" or "hard" by virtue of their longevity or degradability in the environment. Thus, human feces are "soft" whereas pesticides are "hard" or "persistent." Wastes may also be labeled by source, for example, domestic sewage, industrial sewage, or agricultural runoff. However, no single category can embrace the potential for environmental violence. Wastes must be judged on a variety of properties such as toxicity, temperature, volume, decibels, odor, turbidity, synergism, and stability. The very diversity of our huge wasteloads makes wastes so dangerous. A river or an airshed may be able to receive and assimilate much waste, but if just one waste or waste combination proves invincible, then this broad waste-receiving capacity can become defenseless.

in the water

By virtue of their size and extent, our waterways—from mountain streams to the ocean—appear to possess an almost unlimited potential for waste assimilation. However, our diverse wasteloads have already exposed a surprising number of limitations.

The ability of our waterways to absorb organic wastes through dilution and bacterial decomposition is being severely challenged. By concentrating in cities, we concentrate our organic wasteloads. We further concentrate these organic wastes by flushing them down pipes that lead to a main sewage main that may terminate in cavernous splendor at the riverbank. This concentrated demand for decomposition can lead to a proliferation of bacteria that can exhaust a waterway's dissolved oxygen content. Once a waterway's capacity to meet the biological oxygen demand (BOD) is exceeded, septic or anaerobic decomposition—characterized by bacteria which do not need oxygen—can ensue. Undecomposed wastes may settle to the bottom to build up sludge banks. The waterway, and the life in it, can literally suffocate.

Downriver re-aeration can revive an oxygen-depleted waterway. But the proliferation of outfall discharges along a watercourse can serve to counter re-aeration as well as a fish's flight from septic waters. Like a long-distance runner panting for breath, our major rivers, particularly in the industrial East, must try to regain their dissolved oxygen levels from where they begin in the mountains to where they discharge on the ocean shore.

Domestic and industrial sewage treated to lower its BOD level can still release residual waste products. These products are plant nutrients—nitrogen, phosphorous, carbon. Artificial fertilizer runoff from farms, suburban lawns, and golf courses can add to this nutrient load. Although nutrient runoff from the land is essential to the fertility of the waters, increased man-made contributions can distort and subvert biological productivity. High nutrient loads can trigger a profusion or "bloom" of algae that reduces the dissolved oxygen content. As algae blooms decay in the oxygen-poor waters, they settle to the bottom and contribute to sludge build-up and anaerobic conditions. Thus, treated sewage can lead to the same harmful results as raw sewage. Lakes are particularly prone to excessive enrichment or eutrophication because their configuration and circulation patterns serve to constrict the re-aeration process that rivers and streams enjoy. Eutrophication can even "age" a lake—hasten its evolution into a bog clogged with algae, sediment, and undecomposed matter. Lake Erie and Lake Tahoe are well-known lakes troubled by eutrophication.

Large quantities of sewage effluent, even if purged of residual waste products, can overcome the waste-receiving capacity of a waterway. Even effluent treated to 99.5 percent purity can pollute if the total effluent comprises half or more of the water a river carries. Seasonal water fluctuations can complicate this problem. Marine life in an estuary must exist within certain salinity limits; large imputs of effluent can dilute the salinity level and upset the balance necessary for estuarine survival.

A waterway that manages to assimilate spiraling organic wasteloads must still contend with wastes that are inorganic or relatively nondegradable. Such substances resist bacterial attack; dilution and relative immunity from any adverse properties of such substances have always been the waterway's safeguards. The large increase in inorganic wasteloads stemming from materials conversion now challenges these safeguards. Highway bulldozing, subdivision clearing, channel dredging, and strip mining can accelerate erosion and inflate sediment loads that defy ready dilution. Increased water turbidity can screen light needed by photosynthesis processes and by sharp-eyed predators. As the sediment settles, it can bury oysters and other benthic creatures. That sediment can carry other wastes, such as DDT residues or fertilizers, adds to its degrading potential.

Inorganic wastes in minute amounts can be as degrading as huge silt loads. Toxicity makes the difference here. Toxic industrial wastes, such as chlorides, acid mine drainage, and metal salts, can destroy bacteria and thus disarm a river's self-cleaning ability. Oysters and other bivalves tend to filter out and concentrate a wide variety of matter from the surrounding water medium. Such concentrating ability is vital in securing nutrients in the dilute sea solution. However, biological magnification can concentrate zinc, copper, and other trace mineral wastes into lethal agents. In Japan, over 100 residents of a fishing village died after consuming shellfish that had concentrated lethal amounts of a mercury compound that had been discharged into Minamata Bay by a nearby chemical plant. It is noteworthy that the concentrated amount was lethal not to the shellfish but rather to the consumer of the shellfish. The predators at the top of the food pyramid, such as birds and humans, can be particularly prone to the lethal consequences of biological magnification. They can concentrate the accumulated residues at the base of the pyramid.

Radioactive wastes and many of the organic compounds synthesized by the chemical industry are not strictly nondegradable, but they resist bacterial attack and can decay slowly. Like trace mineral wastes, radioactive wastes and organic chemical compounds such as DDT and the chlorinated hydrocarbon pesticides can be taken up in the food web and concentrated in the process of biological magnification. Dr. Charles Wurster of the State University of New York at Stony Brook has related high infant mortality in a seabird, the Bermuda petrel, to uptake of DDT residues. According to Dr. Wurster, the residues can upset enzyme processes and serve to weaken eggshells. Infant deaths from brittle eggshells now threaten the survival of the Bermuda petrel, the brown pelican, the osprey, and the peregrine falcon. These are the creatures at the top of the food pryamid who are fated to sup on the shellfish, which can store DDT at a level 70,000 times greater than that of the surrounding sea solution.

Organic chemical compounds can be released into the environment in amounts that require no biological magnification to be fatal. Shrimp, lobster, crabs, and other crustaceans belong to the same phylum—Arthropoda—as do insects; consequently, insecticide runoff from coastal agricultural and forestry operations can kill nontarget organisms. According to Philip Butler of the Bureau of Commercial Fisheries's Gulf Breeze Laboratory in Florida, heptachlor used in fire-ant control programs washed into an estuary responsible for 60 percent of South Carolina's shrimp catch; a shrimp kill ensued. In developing substances of high toxicity at low concentrations, we are fostering a double-edged efficiency that embraces nontarget as well as target organisms.

The waste-receiving capacity of a waterway may be equal to the organic and inorganic wasteloads it receives but still be rendered ineffective. Thermal or waste heat discharges are, in a sense, degradable. But a waterway, in absorbing such discharges through dilution and mixing, can have its own temperature raised. Power plants withdraw millions of gallons of river water to cool electric generating processes and then return the water to the river at temperatures 20 and 30 degrees F. warmer.

The river's temperature may be raised 10 degrees F. and more. A report by the National Academy of Sciences—National Research Council entitled *Waste Management and Control* observes, "since the amount of dissolved oxygen that can be retained in solution decreases with increasing temperature, the introduction of heat has the same net effect as introducing an oxygen-demanding waste. Increase in temperature thus reduces a stream's waste-assimilative capacity." Fish tend to increase their metabolism in warm temperatures, and abnormally warm temperatures can send them into an uncontrolled frenzy of activity. "The combination of increased need for oxygen and reduced efficiency in obtaining it at rising temperatures can put severe stress even on fishes that ordinarily are capable of living on a meager supply of oxygen," notes John Clark, assistant director of the Sandy Hook Marine Laboratory of the U.S. Bureau of Sport Fisheries and Wildlife, in a *Scientific American* article entitled "Thermal Pollution and Aquatic Life."

Our wasteloads can thus silt up, poison, age, enrich, suffocate, and heat our waterways. In challenging the waste-receiving capacity of a waterway, our wasteloads can be abetted by natural restraints on diluting and mixing processes. Temperature stratification and inversions in water layers can inhibit deep circulation. Seasonal water flow variations can shrink an oxygen-rich river into a waste-sensitive stream. Estuaries tend to circulate discharges rather then transmit them directly to the ocean. This circulation system serves to trap nutrients and foster a rich food base that makes estuaries so productive of wildlife. However, this circulation system will also trap waste discharges and build up organic and inorganic wasteloads to adverse levels. Man-made developments can further shrink the waste-receiving capacity of a waterway. Upstream dams can deny downstream areas of their natural water flow. The compression of estuaries into real estate by filling and bulkheading can restrict tidal flushing and re-aeration. Thus, while increasing our waste discharges, we may be reducing a waterway's capacity to receive wastes.

Groundwater enjoys a filtering and absorption mechanism that surface waters cannot claim, a soil mantle.

Besides putting ground-water resources beyond the pall of direct outfall discharges, the mantle, with its soil bacteria, can destroy organic material during percolation. However, dissolved minerals, salts, and synthetic chemicals can escape this filtering process, and these nondegradable inputs are precisely the type of wastes on the increase. Irrigation drainage, agricultural runoff and septic tank drainage can provide DDT residues, saline waters, mineral fertilizers, and "hard" synthetic detergents. Groundwater lacks the ability to regenerate itself through aeration and circulation to the degree that surface waters enjoy, and thus ground-water contamination can persist even though the dissolved mineral input may be temporary.

Even the ocean, the personification of natural strength, is challenged by the wasteload assault. As the brittle eggshells suggest, the sharp rise in toxic synthetic and inorganic compounds can haunt the entire ocean food web. The sheer volume of organic wasteloads, concentrated in mammoth offshore outfalls, raises the potential for excessive enrichment. Submarine forests of a giant seaweed, bladder kelp, have been receding into ghost forests off southern California. Marine ecologist Wheeler North of the California Institute of Technology noticed that small sea urchins were piling up locust-like in the denuded forests. These small seabed creatures graze on kelp. That a principal urchin predator, the sea otter, was nearly exterminated by fur hunters in the nineteenth century has lifted one natural control on urchin populations. However, after grazing on kelp, the urchins normally move on to allow the kelp forest to regenerate. Dr. North wondered what caused urchins to remain stationary in a denuded kelp forest. He observed that the kelp forests that were receding were within the vicinity of offshore outfalls. Laboratory and field tests sponsored by the U.S. Public Health Service and conducted by Dr. North, Dr. David Leighton and Dr. Mary Clark showed that urchins can absorb through their skin dissolved organic matter, especially amino acids, released by sewage discharges. Concentrations of amino acids and other dissolved materials in the marine environment are four to five times greater near outfalls. Each day coastal cities in southern

California discharge a half million gallons of sewage into offshore waters. Dr. North links this excessive enrichment to the newly assumed stationary nature of the urchins and the resulting inability of the kelp forests to regenerate. With support from state conservation agencies and a private kelp harvester, Dr. North now quick-limes urchins to revive the kelp forests.

Without even living in the ocean, we can subvert its ecology in the same careless manner that the land has been exposed to. It is almost as if desecration has been computerized and put on remote control. And behind this desecration lurk our spiraling wasteloads.

in the air

Like our large waterways, the atmosphere would appear to have an almost unlimited capacity for waste-receiving. Although not endowed with waste-eating bacteria, the atmosphere has great dispersion and mixing properties, and this vaunted assimilative capacity becomes a free good, open to all. However, this waste-receiving capacity, just as in the case of our waterways, can be sharply limited by natural restraints. Winds, when blowing in sufficient strength, can disperse emissions horizontally over a wide area. Warm air and warm emissions tend to rise and be vertically displaced, as long as the air above is cooler. Sometimes an air mass can be stable, with little or no temperature change with altitude increase. An increase in temperature with altitude can foster an inversion. Like a temperature inversion in a lake or an ocean, a temperature inversion in an air mass can halt vertical circulation and contain emissions close to the ground. The "lid" effect can be intensified by topographical features, such as mountains that can corral waste emissions in the basin below. Spanish explorers once referred to a location along the southern California coast as the Bay of Smokes because Indian smoke fires literally fanned out. Weak winds, temperature inversions, and basin topography fostered the smoky stratification. Today, the location, Los Angeles, contends with smog because of "an unholy alliance between a substantial daily dose of aerial contaminants and a highly variable amount of natural ventilation," according to UCLA meteorologist James Edinger (see Figures 1–3). Los Angeles is treated to temperature inversions on an average of 260 days per year. Fog and low clouds can also foster inversions such as those along the eastern seaboard. Appalachia and the southeast porton of the United States frequently suffer poor air dilution because of slow-moving anticyclones that stagnate for four days and more (see Table 1 and Figure 4).

Because of variations in ventilation, the atmosphere can be broken down regionally into airsheds. However, as the California Air Resources Agency observes, "Unlike watersheds, it is not possible to define air basins wherein the air pollution problems would be completely isolated from adjacent basins. Winds do not start and stop at political and geographic boundaries."

The wasteloads that affect our waterways stem primarily from materials conversion. The wasteloads that affect our airsheds stem primarily from energy conversion. The burning of fossil fuels—coal, natural gas, and petroleum—discharges gases, aerosols, and particulate matter into the air. Nuclear energy adds another discharge: radioactivity. Manufacturing processes may give off metallic fumes, acid mists, and fluorides while soil erosion may greatly increase dust emissions. Agricultural spray operations can discharge chemical residues into the air. Paints and solvents can give off aerosols. However, the sheer number of sources, from auto engines to power plants, as well as the diverse composition of the emissions makes energy conversion the single most important waste influence on airsheds (see Figure 5).

Fossil-fuel combustion can discharge hydrocarbons, oxides of nitrogen, carbon dioxide, carbon monoxide, sulfur dioxide, and soot. Carbon dioxide and carbon monoxide are relatively stable, but hydrocarbons, oxides of nitrogen, and sulfur compounds are unstable and subject to synergism. When an airshed is pressed beyond its waste-receiving capacity, these emissions and their synergistic by-products can accumulate and change the composition of the air. The change can make life-giving air both toxic and corrosive. Hydrocarbons and oxides of nitrogen, in their original form, are relatively harmless. Yet, when combined under sunlight, they can generate

figure 1. *The Los Angeles City Hall during a clear day.*

figure 2. *Smog engulfs the Los Angeles City Hall when a temperature inversion 1500 feet high prohibits dispersion of air contaminants into upper atmosphere.*

the
planet
as dump

figure 3. Smog is trapped by a temperature inversion at 300 feet above the ground. Inversions are present over the Los Angeles basin approximately 320 days of the year.

Photos by Los Angeles County Air Pollution Control District.

the ozone that is associated with eye irritation, respiratory complications, vegetation damage, and rubber cracking. Sulfur compounds can be converted into sulfuric acid mists that attack building surfaces and complicate respiration.

Carbon monoxide has the ability to impair the oxygen-carrying capacity of the bloodstream. Carbon dioxide in very high concentrations can affect cardiac control. Lead aerosols from gasoline or paint, asbestos fibers, pesticide sprays, and radioactive emissions are examples of other discharges that can accumulate to potentially toxic levels. Living organisms may inhale these substances directly or take them up in the food web through fallout on land and in water. Accidental discharges in chemical and biological warfare research can also inject toxic emissions into airsheds.

An airshed can also be subject to atmospheric turbidity. Once more the chief culprit is fossil-fuel combustion.

table 1

**description of atmospheric areas and their characteristics,
air quality act of 1967, section 107(a)(1)**

atmospheric area	extent of area	meteorological and topographical characteristics
California-Oregon coastal area	Extends about 20 to 50 miles inland from the Pacific Ocean.	Maritime air penetration, prevailing shallow vertical mixing depths; topographic restraints on ventilation in coastal valleys and basins.
Washington coastal area	Extends about 20 to 30 miles inland from the Puget Sound region, from which the eastern boundary extends southwestward to the vicinity of Longview on the Columbia River and then westward to the coast.	Precipitation, cloudiness, and relatively high winds are dominant features of the climate, which distinguishes this area from the adjacent areas. Storm activity is frequent, particularly during winter and spring seasons; the frequent storm passages result in a low occurrence of persistent stagnation.
Rocky Mountain area	Extends eastward from the California-Oregon and Washington coastal areas, to terminate as a north-south oriented eastern boundary, essentially corresponding to the 3,000- to 4,000-foot mean sea level contour interval which in general defines the eastern-most extension of the major mountain ranges. This eastern boundary stretches from the Canadian border in Montana southward through extreme eastern Colorado, eastern New Mexico, to the Mexican border, to include the Big Bend region of Texas.	Topographic restriction, channeling of winds, particularly frequent surface-based inversions at night, and relatively deep mixing depths during the afternoon are prevalent features of the dilution climate of the area.
Great Plains area	Extends eastward from the Rocky Mountain area to the Mississippi River south of Missouri; to the north it includes most of Illinois, southwestern Indiana, southwestern Wisconsin, and all but extreme northeast Minnesota.	Relatively flat terrain, which stretches from the Canadian border to the Gulf of Mexico, characterizes the topography. The dilution climate is characterized by negligible persistent atmospheric stagnation and the frequent occurrence of relatively high winds with rapidly changing meteorological conditions.

Great Lakes-Northeast area	In addition to regions adjacent to the Great Lakes, this area includes the northern two-thirds of the States of Indiana and Ohio, the Allegheny Plateau area of northwestern Pennsylvania, all of New York State but the extreme southern part of the Hudson River Valley, and the New England States north of the Connecticut-Rhode Island coastal area.	The meteorology is characterized by frequent storm passages with attendant high winds and generally good dilution conditions. During the spring and early summer months, winds blowing from over the cold waters of the Great Lakes and Atlantic Ocean enhance low-level stability in regions adjacent to these bodies of water.
Appalachian area	The eastern boundary of this area, which extends from northern New Jersey southward through southeastern Pennsylvania, eastern Virginia to the Atlantic coastline at the South Carolina border, is correlative for the most part with the 300- to 500-feet mean sea level contour interval. This contour interval at the foothills of the Blue Ridge Mountain Range distinguishes the relatively flat coastal plain to the east from the Appalachian Mountains. The area extends southward to the Gulf of Mexico, including northern Florida, and is bounded in the west and north by two other atmospheric areas.	Dominant features of the dilution climate include light wind speeds and the most frequent stagnation conditions of any region east of the Rocky Mountains.
Mid-Atlantic coastal area	Encompasses the Atlantic coastal plain from extreme southwestern Connecticut, including the New York City and Long Island region, southward to the South Carolina border at the coastline, and extends inland to the Appalachian area.	Shallow mixing depths, less frequent low-level stability and higher wind speeds are features of the dilution climate that distinguish this coastal area from those adjacent.
South Florida area	Extends south from the Daytona Beach-Cedar Key line to include the southern half of Florida.	The climate of this area is predominantly tropical-marine in nature. Atmospheric stagnation is practically nonexistent; there is a small frequency of low-level stability; and relatively good vertical mixing prevails.

Source: Federal Register, vol. 33, no. 10.

25

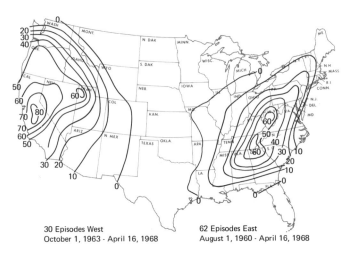

30 Episodes West
October 1, 1963 - April 16, 1968

62 Episodes East
August 1, 1960 - April 16, 1968

figure 4. *Isopleths of total number of forecast days of high air pollution potential since forecasting began.*

Source: G. C. Holzworth, "Large-scale Weather Influences on Air Pollution in the U.S.," presented at 61st annual meeting, APC, St. Paul, Minn., June, 1968.

Sulfur emissions can accumulate under a low ceiling of fogs and clouds and foster a turbid condition generally referred to as smaze or smog. Cities that use heating fuels with a high-sulfur content, such as New York and London, have been particularly susceptible. In contrast, Los Angeles's photochemical smog depends on the "cooking" action of sunlight on auto emissions such as oxides of nitrogen and hydrocarbons. While sulfur-based smog can continue around the clock, photochemical smog comes and goes with the sun. Dust storms generated by soil erosion can generate another form of atmospheric turbidity.

Besides intensifying potential exposure to toxic agents, atmospheric turbidity reduces visibility and the corresponding physical ability to see. UCLA meteorologist Norris Neiburger compared visibility ranges in Los Angeles before and after the advent of noticeable smog in 1941. Eliminating effects of various weather conditions, he found frequency of observations of visibility greater than 12 miles at noon in the period from 1932–1937 was 30 percent; in 1944–1949 it was only 18 percent. In *Air*

the
planet
as dump

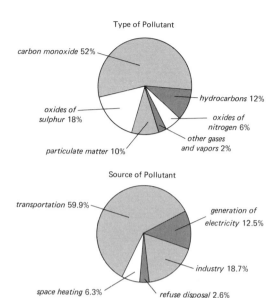

figure 5. Air pollution in the United States (125 millon tons per year).

Source: "Waste Management and Control," report to the Federal Council for Science and Technology by the Commission on Pollution, National Academy of Sciences—National Research Council, 1966.

Pollution, Leslie Chambers raises another potentially foreboding aspect to increased air turbidity: "The attenuation of ultraviolet and other radiations reaching the surface through layers of aerosols may be associated with adverse physiological effects in men and vegetation." Solar ultraviolet radiation generates natural vitamin D in the human body.

Atmospheric turbidity can also lead to damaging fallout. Particulate fallout from turbid airsheds can be deposited on living organisms and physical structures. Besides dirt and soot, these deposits can contain toxic and corrosive agents the particulates have picked up in the air.

Carbon dioxide is, next to water vapor, the largest single waste emission generated by the burning of fossil fuels. Carbon dioxide is naturally abundant in the atmosphere and we are well adapted to living with widely varying levels of it. Carbon dioxide helps maintain the over-all temperature of the earth through its insulating effect. Some scientists are concerned that increased concentrations of carbon dioxide from fossil-fuel burning could serve to heat the atmosphere drastically (the "greenhouse" effect). Other scientists disagree, saying that increased atmospheric turbidity could serve to screen out the sun's rays and decrease temperatures drastically.

It has been observed that an urban area is generally more cloudy, foggy, and rainy than its surrounding area. Climatologist Stanley Changnon, Jr., of the Illinois State Water Survey now links urban air emissions to increased urban humidity. Heat emissions from industrial activities and other sources cause the air over a city to rise and mix, a condition necessary for cloud formation. Particulate matter acts as a nuclei around which water and fog droplets can form. According to Dr. Changnon, Chicago received 7.53 inches more of rain than surrounding areas between 1959 and 1968 because of air pollution's weather-making ability. The North Atlantic jet flyways are now more permanently cloud-covered than in earlier days, a change that has been attributed to cloud-seeding by vapor trails. Dr. V. J. Schaefer, director of Atmospheric Sciences Research Center, Albany, N.Y., predicts that a fleet of supersonic transports discharging 150,000 tons of vapor daily could produce an atmospheric condition that would obscure the sun.

If our waterways, including the ocean, exhibit the broad impact of our wasteloads in the environment, our airsheds reflect the potential depth of this impact. By exceeding the waste-receiving capacity of our airsheds, our wasteloads may be altering the climate of the world. That there is no firm evidence that such climatic alteration will ensue is hardly cause for complacency. Traditionally, recognition of waste pollution has been dependent on highly visible consequences, such as fish kills or discolored skies. Accordingly, the question of climatic alteration may be resolved only when we begin to shiver or sweat profusely. Our wasteloads can exceed both the limitations of our knowledge and the natural environment.

on eardrums

The ability of living organisms to absorb another increasing waste emission—unwanted sound or noise—is also being rigorously tested. The natural environment is relatively quiet; this quality in the desert, the forest, the prairie, and the submarine kelp forests is a principal attraction for noise-buffeted city residents. This quiet nature stems less from natural sound absorption and acoustics than from a paucity of sounds. Volcanic eruptions, thunder, surf and waterfalls aside, nature rarely speaks above the rustle of a leaf or the babble of a brook. Even that momentous rumbling inside the planet, an earthquake, is gently muffled.

This natural quietness is of vital importance to animals. In this stillness, the bird and the moose can call their mates readily across the wilderness. Enemies that cannot be seen can be exposed by the mere crack of a twig. Unknown sound instinctively "startles" an animal into alertness, making his heart beat faster and his muscles and nerves taut.

The shattering of this strategic stillness is a distinctive attribute of man's machinery. The beat of the pneumatic street drill, the wail of the siren, the shriek of brakes, the whine of jets and now, even in the stillness of the winter forest, the engine noise of the snowmobile—all serve to fill the environment with aural discord. By using the environment as a noise sink, we can disrupt critical communication and continually startle nerve systems into fatigue. Acute doses of noise can induce deafness; continuing subacute doses can impair hearing. For animals especially dependent on sound, such as bats, sonar-sensory marine mammals, and blind people, continuing noise can rob them of their security. Sonic booms imbue noise with another dangerous attribute—shock waves that can make cliffs and windows vibrate.

on the land

Our land, generally, has been less affected by our wasteloads than air, water, or eardrums. This is not because the land has a better waste-receiving capacity. It lacks both the dispersive capabilities of the atmosphere and the dilution capabilities of a waterway. Although organic waste matter will decompose on land, the rate of decomposition is generally slower than in a waterway. Whereas, soil tends to bond and render inert many synthetic chemicals or mineral wastes, certain residues may still be taken up in the food web, as in the waterways. Radioactive strontium has been absorbed by plants and entered the food chain of milk cattle and man. Heptachlor epoxide, a persistent pesticide that defies soil bacteria, has been ingested by earthworms and concentrated in worm-feeding birds. The soil's ability to support plants and animal crops has not been appreciably affected by biological magnification, but the long-term build-up of radioactive wastes and persistent pesticides could change this.

Land-water interchange has made the land more resistant to wastes. Waste substances on land that are water-soluble or relatively bouyant often wind up in the water; thus radioactive wastes, pesticide residues, residual organic wastes, chemicals and old tires are transferred to the nearest waterway by rains and floods. Trace mineral salts and synthetic chemicals percolate down through the soil and into ground water. Hence, the land has the ability to transfer the burden of waste-receiving to the water. Our kitchen grinders and toilets have served to intensify this transfer. The wastes the air may transfer to the land are generally light enough to be drained into waterways. Even if ocean tides transfer old telephone poles and other debris to the land, junk flotsam hardly serves to even up the exchange.

The sheer volume and changing nature of our wasteloads serve to undermine the land's apparent resistance to wastes. City-generated solid wastes far exceed the wastes brought about by natural decomposition and land-water interchange. Food and agricultural wastes that accumulate can putrefy and exude gaseous odors, such as hydrogen sulfide and methane, into the air. Gases that cannot escape into the air may build up pressures within accumulated refuse. Some of these gases, such as methane, are highly combustible.

The process of putrefaction can engender a perverse biological enrichment in the form of rat and fly colonies. The nonputrescent matter, such as old sofas and tires, can provide convenient shelter for refuse life. A cubic foot of garbage can produce 75,000 flies. Following ingestion of human and animal excreta, flies can become carriers of infectious diseases. Some flies will drop their eggs in excreta, which may also hasten the spread of disease. Organic matter that does not putrefy, such as wood and paper, may be combustible and create a fire-hazard situation, particularly where methane gases are present.

Organic refuse will eventually, albeit slowly, decompose, but nondegradable refuse persists; this type of refuse is on the increase. The nondegradable, nonreturnable, one-use product that is making such an impression in the marketplace is also making its own indelible impression on the environment, from the beer can on the seabed to the mountain of junk autos outside Los Angeles. Like the nondegradable residues of radioactivity and trace minerals building up in our food web, the nondegradable trash is building up on our landscape. The danger in the trash build-up, however, does not lie in potential toxic consequences. The trash build-up tends to consume open land at the same time that land demands increase. Official dumps—junkyards, municipal dumps, cemeteries—and unofficial dumps—road shoulders, empty lots, flood control channels, riverbanks—are proliferating. Some cities may literally be ringed by official and unofficial dumps (see Figures 6 and 7).

in total

By overcoming the waste-receiving capacity of the natural environment, our wastes have demonstrated their ability to alter the environment. The release of a waste into the environment does not by itself mean that the environment is going to be degraded or polluted. The fertility of our waterways, for instance, can be enhanced to a certain degree by organic enrichment. The wastes that interfere with or defy the waste-receiving capacity of the environment create the pollution. The degree and the intensity of this interference are growing as our wasteloads grow. In the case of increased atmospheric turbidity, we are not even certain of the full implications of interference.

figure 6. *Scrap iron yard usurps scenic San Francisco Bay shore.*

The natural environment possesses vast regenerative powers. A waterway can revive from temporary septic conditions while a dirty airshed can be cleansed by winds. However, the continuous nature and volume of our waste discharges interferes with and even suppresses these regenerative powers. An oxygen-poor waterway purged of life forms will lose the ability to repopulate and support life. A waterway purged of only very pollution-sensitive life forms will still lose species diversity. As the report *Waste Management and Control* notes, "Diversity means stability in any natural system, because it means many alternatives. If something happens to one pathway, others are available for the flow of energy through the system." The rise of inorganic and synthetic chemical wastes that are relatively nondegradable and can build up to potentially toxic levels increases the potential for irreversible alterations from waste pollution. Once a bird species loses its ability to reproduce through the perverse consequences of biological magnification, it is lost forever.

Waste pollution, because of its broad ability to alter natural systems, has become a principal feature of our urban environment, where waste-making is concentrated. Our 22 major waterways display all or some of the symptoms of pollution: fish kills, discolored water, septic odors, scum algae, low-dissolved oxygen, excessive turbidity. Most of our major cities, poorly ventilated or well ventilated, look up at airsheds discolored by waste emissions, including the "Windy City," Chicago.

Waste pollution promises to be amplified and become a major global phenomenon. Once a waterway loses its waste-assimilative capacity, it passes on wastes to the coastal ocean, already under pressure from outfall wasteloads and radioactive and pesticide fallout. Activities that generate wastes with a formidable pollution potential—atomic energy, supersonic airplanes, power plants with large-scale thermal discharges—have yet to reach their full development. The automobile that generates photochemical smog, as well as the throwaway container, is in relative infancy. The trend in synthetic chemicals toward stable compounds with powerful properties

figure 7. *Junk auto heaps become a common part of the urban landscape.*

in low concentrations continues. Thus the natural interchange between land, air and water, so vital in recycling life-giving water, nutrients and oxygen, recycles and magnifies more and more chemicals alien to the natural environment.

The high Uinta Mountains of Utah, populated by cougars, elk, otter, and alpine lake trout, rank as one of this nation's most primitive wilderness areas. Yet the trout are the most radioactive of their species in the entire state, according to a *National Observer* interview with biologist Robert Pendleton of the University of Utah. Radiation levels in the soils and some plants, although low, were five and seven times higher in 1969 than in 1962, when the first samples were taken. One of the few American ranges running from east to west, the Uinta Mountains stand in the direct path of fallout clouds from nuclear tests 400 miles southwest, in Nevada. Although underground, in accord with limited nuclear-test-ban treaty, the tests still release enough radioactivity to infiltrate the Uinta ecosystem. Snow and rain wash radioactive residues into lower valleys to build up in reservoirs and irrigated farms. Student investigators for Dr. Pendleton have now found a name for one unnamed Uinta: Atomic Peak.

Natural water and air are becoming rather rare commodities. Natural air no longer exists in the mainland United States, not even in Yellowstone National Park, the Grand Canyon or the other official "outdoors." To find unadulterated air, completely devoid of waste traces, we must go to the mid-Pacific or mid-Atlantic. In both these areas, oceanographers have found abnormal lead and radioactive levels in water samples, indicative of the ocean's role as the ultimate sink.

In the desolate Sargasso Sea of the Atlantic Ocean, oceanographic nets became so fouled with oil and tar residues that towing became impossible during a recent Woods Hole marine expedition. Global contamination such as this has been generated largely by the industrial activities of a minority of the world's population.

To what extent waste pollution as a *global* phenomenon will alter the environment is not known. Our ability to recognize the implications of waste pollution has been largely dependent on visible consequences, such as fish kills and discolored skies. Whereas our measuring instruments can pick up minute amounts of contamination, our existing knowledge falls short of even interpreting the potential for weather alteration. As our wasteloads expand, so do the risks of waste pollution. A basic ecological force—waste assimilation and recycling—is thus being transformed into an anti-ecological force of waste pollution. This transformation affects not only our environment but also our existence.

SUGGESTED READINGS

GENERAL

National Academy of Sciences, *Waste Management and Control,* Washington, D.C.: National Academy of Sciences–National Research Council, pub. no. 1400, 1966, appendixes 1, 3, 4.

Office of Science and Technology, Department of Agriculture, *Control of Agriculture-Related Pollution,* report to the President, 1969.

IN THE WATER

Clark, John, "Thermal Pollution," *Scientific American,* March, 1969.

Kneese, Allen, and Blair Bower, *Managing Water Quality: Economics, Technology and Institutions,* Baltimore: Johns Hopkins Press, 1968, chap. 2. Published for Resources for the Future.

Kurland, Leonard, Stanley Fard, and Howard Siedler, "Minamata Disease," *World Neurology,* November, 1960.

Marx, Wesley, *The Frail Ocean,* New York: Coward-McCann, 1967, chap. 4 (on kelp recession); Ballantine paperback, 1969.

ZoBell, Claude, "The Occurrence, Effects and Fate of Oil Polluting the Sea," *Proceedings, International Conference on Water Pollution Research, 1962.* London: Pergamon Press, 1962.

man and his environment: waste

Department of the Interior, *Surface Mining and Our Environment,* Washington, D.C.: U.S. Government Printing Office, 1967.

IN THE AIR

National Academy of Sciences–National Research Council, *Weather and Climate Modification—Problems and Prospects,* Washington, D.C.: National Academy of Sciences–National Research Council, pub. no. 1350, 2 vols., 1966.

Stern, Arthur, ed., *Air Pollution,* 2nd ed., New York: Academic Press, 1968, vol. I, pts. 1 and 3.

ON EARDRUMS

Beranek, L. L., "Noise," *Scientific American,* December, 1966.

PESTICIDES

Butler, Philip, and Paul Springer, "Pesticides—A New Factor in Coastal Environments," *Transactions, 28th North American Wildlife and Natural Resources Conference,* 1963.

Carson, Rachel, *The Silent Spring,* New York: Houghton Mifflin, 1962.

Laycock, George, "Where Have All the Pelicans Gone?" *Audubon,* September, 1969.

Rudd, Robert, *Pesticides and the Living Landscape,* Madison: University of Wisconsin Press, 1964.

RADIATION

Eisenbud, Merrill, *Environmental Radioactivity,* New York: McGraw-Hill, 1963.

Schaefer, Milner, "Some Fundamental Aspects of Marine Ecology in Relation to Radioactive Wastes." *Contributions,* La Jolla, Calif.: Scripps Institute of Oceanography, 1960, new series.

4
the dump spills over

We do not appear to be in as intimate and vulnerable contact with the natural environment as the Bermuda petrel and the smog-smitten flowers. We live in artificial shelters in man-made settings. Machines provide us with energy, motor power, and materials. We play games on artificial grass by the light of electricity. We swim in artificial pools and lakes. In our man-made setting, the natural environment appears to recede into segregated patches of wilderness, accessible via camper vacations and Boy Scout outings. Yet the natural environment remains our life-support system. As do birds and flowers, we rely on it for water, nutrients, and air. Ironically, only by using the environment as a dump have we learned the degree to which we remain reliant on it.

the threats to health
In the 1800s, cities were periodically ravaged by typhoid epidemics. Bacterial organisms in drinking water were identified as the disease carrier. These organisms, not natural to the waterways that provided drinking water, were released into lakes and rivers via the feces of infected humans.

Man's traditional response to waste pollution has been an up-turned nose. Even today, a principal feeling aroused by the world "waste" is redolent smells of urine, rotten eggs, baby diapers, and putrefying garbage. The typhoid epidemics dramatically illustrated how our wastes could affect our health as well as our nostrils. The emergence of the germ theory of disease revealed this impact of our wastes. Other carriers of infectious diseases were revealed in the forms of rats and flies fattening up on garbage dumps. Static land dumps would not appear to be as effective a carrier of germs as water; however, garbage flies can travel as far as 20 miles.

Extinguishing thousands of lives in one fell swoop without either the victim or the perpetrator knowing it would appear to be virtually impossible. Yet, as the typhoid epidemics demonstrated, innocent use of the natural environment as both life-support system and dump can accomplish this task (see Figure 8). Biological magnification of our increasing nondegradable waste discharges—as occurred in Minamata Bay—expands the toxic potential of our waterways. Our use of waterways as food, recreational, and water sources can broaden our exposure to this toxic potential.

In this century, another form of waste pollution evidenced its silent ability to trigger mass mortality. In December, 1930, a dense layer of fog and smog hung low over the Meuse Valley of Belgium. People throughout the 15-mile-long valley complained of difficulty in breathing. During the three-day seige of acute air pollution, the average mortality rate was exceeded by 63. At the time, one medical investigator, J. Firket, observed that the "public services of London might be faced with the responsibility of 3200 sudden deaths if such a phenomenon occurred there." During October, 1948, Donora, Pennsylvania, experienced an acute air pollution crisis. Some 43 percent of the city's 14,000 residents felt ill and were seized by fits of coughing and vomiting. The excessive mortality rate during the four-day pollution seige rose to 17. From December 5–9, 1952, a dense layer of fog and smog blanketed London and Mr. Firket was deemed a prophet. The excessive mortality rate shot up to 4000. A year later New York experienced an acute air pollution episode and an excessive mortality rate of 200. London has since experienced three more acute air pollution episodes, New York two (see Table 2).

the
dump
spills
over

These acute air pollution episodes challenge medical knowledge as well as human health. There is no name for the disease or causative agent behind the excessive mortality rates because none has been identified. The present field of medicine is highly effective in identifying direct cause-and-effect relationships in disease, such as infectious germs. It is much less able to relate compound or synergistic effects to illness and morality; it is these effects that are a prime characteristic of air pollution,

figure 8. *Chemical waste/human disease pathways (postulated).*

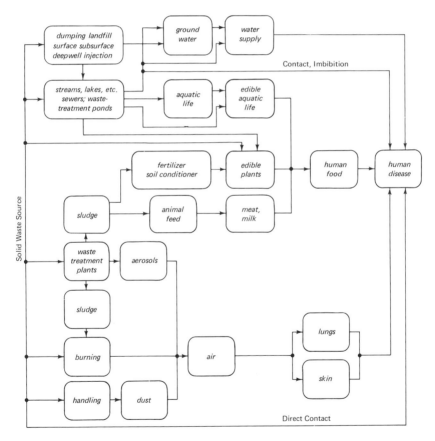

Source: Hanks, Thrift, Solid Waste—Disease Relationships, 1967 report prepared by Aerojet-General Corporation under contract to Solid Wastes Program, Department of Health, Education, and Welfare, Public Health Service pub. no. 999-UIH-6.

table 2
mortality during episodes of air pollution

date	place	sulfur dioxide value (peak)	mortality
Feb., 1880	London	—	1000
Dec., 1930	Meuse Valley	9.6–38.4 ppm[a]	63
Oct., 1948	Donora	2.0 ppm	17[b]
Dec., 1952	London	1.47 ppm	4000
Jan., 1956	London	—	1000
Dec., 1957	London	—	700–800
Dec., 1962	London	same as 1952	700
Nov., 1953	New York	0.86 ppm	200
Jan.–Feb., 1963	New York	0.40–1.50 ppm	200–400
Nov., 1966	New York	0.69–0.97–1.02 ppm	168

[a] Assumed retrospectively.
[b] These deaths are usually counted in the literature as 20. Actually, only 19 occurred during the week and two deaths were the usual expected per week.

Source: M. C. Battigelli, "Sulfur Dioxide and Acute Effects of Air Pollution," Air Quality Criteria Symposium, New York, June 4–5, 1968.

given the extraordinary mixture of waste discharges that an airshed receives. The acute air pollution episodes occurred in cities where fossil fuels with a high sulfur content are burned. Sulfur emissions transformed into sulfuric acid mists can collect on particulate matter and can be inhaled. As Dr. Eric Cassell of New York notes, "One has, in effect, inhaled a tiny sulfuric acid factory." This tiny factory can complicate breathing and has been put forth as the causative agent for excessive mortality. Laboratory tests on this relationship, however, are inconclusive. Writing in the *Archives of Industrial Hygiene and Occupational Medicine,* I. Greenwald observes, "Sulfur dioxide and sulfuric acid can neither be held responsible for the Meuse Valley, Donora and London episodes nor be absolved from at least partial responsibility." Individual tolerances to acute air pollution exposures varied. Persons most susceptible generally had a history of respiratory or cardiovascular disease. This susceptibility might reaffirm the respiratory irritant action of sulfuric acid mists or reflect lower resistance in general to stressful conditions. The variations in susceptibility suggest that an acute air pollution episode is toxic not in itself but only in combination with other known and unknown factors. Dr. R. Frank of the Harvard University School of Public Health observes, "The constituents of air pollution are many, are complex, and are not completely known; they have the potential for additive, cumulative and synergistic effect; they may interact with age, smoking, climate, and ill health, to cite only a partial list." In an article in the *Archives of Environmental Health,* Dr. L. Greenburg and a group of medical investigators note that the mortality peak in New York's 1963 acute air pollution episode was "the result of unusual stresses, air pollution, influenza, and cold weather, acting on the population simultaneously."

Photochemical smog has yet to be implicated in an air pollution "disaster." Its dissipation during the evening hours provides one safeguard against continuous exposure to acute levels. However, the daytime build-up of potentially toxic synergistic products like ozone concerns members of the medical profession in Los Angeles. In an interview with Los Angeles radio station KLAC, Dr. Joseph Boyle, president of the Los Angeles Medical Association, remarked, "I believe that we have at least three times this year [1967] been in a position where, had the climatic conditions persisted for very many days longer, or had the atmosphere conditions changed just a very little bit, that we could have had, perhaps not the same kind of Donora-type disaster, but something which would have been of rather dramatic proportions." Although the scientific and medical professions may have no universal explanation of the lethal consequences of acute air pollution episodes, they do agree on the import of these episodes. "The evidence that is available demonstrates beyond any reasonable doubt that air pollution is guilty of killing and disabling people and that it is capable of doing far more widespread damage than it has already done," observes Dr. John Middleton of the National Air Pollution Control Center. By using our natural air supply as well as our natural water supply as a dump, we can expose our health to even greater risks. Forewarned, we can refrain from drinking polluted water; abstaining from breathing is another matter. The average adult requires 30 pounds of air daily. He can live five days without water but only five minutes without air.

The case of acute sound emissions that have resulted

in severe hearing damage have yet to occur in the general environment. Hearing loss in occupational settings, however, has already been reported. U.S. servicemen in tank weapons practice have been exposed to noise levels of 135 decibels—above the pain level. They have been exposed to 164 decibels on the rifle range, far above the 150-decibel damage point. As a result, these servicemen may go into combat with diminished hearing capacity. Commercial jets and supersonic airplanes expose ground crews to such damaging decibel levels that earmuffs and soundproofing are necessary in airport areas. Neighboring residents are not similarly protected, and we face the possibility that a jet or one of the new supersonic airliners, perhaps on a low takeoff, through a navigation error, in a hijacking episode, or because of an emergency air manuever may expose an entire city to an acute dose of noise, as well as a crash and its resultant disasters.

Such acute exposures form dramatic but by no means the only health threats that waste pollution generates. Continuous exposure to low-level but cumulative contaminants can produce chronic health effects and delayed damage. Once more, the rise of relatively nondegradable compounds and the increasing opportunities for exposure in air, water, and food sources helps create the potential for harm. Chronic effects can be seen in occupational settings. Inhalation of asbestos dust by construction workers can cause a serious, often fatal, lung disease, asbestosis. Factory workers continually exposed to loud but not severe noise levels have suffered hearing losses. Children who have ingested paint chips containing lead additives have accumulated lead levels that damaged the brain.

Epidemiological studies have related high incidences of chronic bronchitis, lung cancer, and emphysema to populations exposed to relatively high levels of air pollution. Studies in Great Britain, for instance, have showed a very close correlation between residency in cities troubled with air pollution and occurrence of chronic bronchitis. Construction workers only lightly exposed to asbestos dust did not die of asbestosis but showed a very high death rate from lung cancer.

*the
dump
spills
over*

The hazards posed by continuous exposure to contaminants go beyond toxicity and include carcinogenicity (the production of cancer) and mutagenicity (the production of genetic damage). Cancer-inducing agents such as a polynuclear hydrocarbon, benzo[a]pyrene, have been identified as atmospheric pollutants. Administration of pollutant extracts to newborn mice has resulted in a high incidence of liver, lung, and blood cancers.

In 1926, Dr. Hermann Joseph Muller observed that heavy doses of x-rays applied to fruit flies could increase mutation rates or genetic changes in their offspring. Amost four decades later, Dr. Muller warned a Food and Drug Administration conference of other agents that may become chemical mutagens for man as well as fruit flies: "Today, we human beings are exposed to a great number of substances not encountered by our ancestors, to which we therefore have not been specifically adapted by natural selection. Among these substances are food additives, drugs, narcotics, antibiotics, pesticides, cosmetics, contraceptives, air pollutants and water pollutants." A gene mutation can express itself immediately as an early fetal death or as dwarfism, excess fingers, or cancer of the retina of the eye in the surviving offspring. However, as the FDA notes, "It is the recessive mutation that especially troubles scientists, since its detriments or defects may not express themselves for several generations after there is a union of two carriers of the same recessive mutant gene." Whereas only a small part of the substances we have devised have been evaluated for mutagenic activity, the early evaluations are not very comforting for a society that so indiscriminately releases pesticides, synthetic detergents, and other man-made chemicals into the environment. A 1968 National Institutes of Health genetic study observed, "Recent investigations have revealed chemical compounds that are highly mutagenic in experimental organisms in concentrations that are not toxic and that have no overt effect on fertility."

Increasingly concerned by the implications of long-term low-level exposures, medical science is limited in its ability to identify the exact scope of the health threat. Because the study of carcinogenicity and of mutagenicity are both in their relative infancy, full identification of cancer and mutagenic agents must await considerable basic research. Dr. John Hanlon informed an HEW conference, "In all, the public is exposed to about 500,000 different substances but fewer than 10 percent have been studied and catalogued in a meaningful fashion, and much less in relation to each other and the other factors in man and his environment." As in the case of acute exposures to waste pollution, a number of potential causitive agents must be considered and analyzed. Synergism once more serves to complicate the picture. For example, the Food and Drug Administration finds itself investigating drug-pesticide interaction. As FDA official Clara Williams observes in an article in the FDA *Papers,* "Administration of the tranquilizing drug chlorpromazine increased the toxicity to a crop-spraying worker of the organophosphate pesticide parathion." The study of such interactions hardly reflects the relative simplicity of germ-disease vectors. "Even though the chemical structure of both the drug and the pesticide may be known, their metabolic interaction cannot be predicted solely upon this basis because of the complex metabolic capabilities which man and animals possess and because of the wide variations in body mechanisms within a particular species and between different species," notes Dr. Williams.

The time factor expands the range of causitive agents that must be considered. In the case of the construction workers exposed to asbestos dust, exposure and subsequent deaths from lung cancer often covered a period of 20 years. Epidemiological studies that isolated this association also noted a high incidence of cigarette smoking among lung-cancer victims. In fact, lung cancer only occurred among asbestos workers who were smokers. "Smoking asbestos workers had eight times as much lung cancer as cigarette smokers not exposed to asbestos," observed Dr. Cuyler Hammond, Department of Epidemiology, American Cancer Society, before a Congressional committee. "The present impression is that asbestos works as a cocarcinogenic agent, enormously increasing the cancer-producing potential of cigarette smoking. This is why I am worried about combinations of agents rather than simply looking for one agent that is harmful in itself."

Victims of low-level exposures may be left just as much in the dark as medical investigators. Persons who suffer hearing losses from continuous exposure to loud but not severe noise levels generally do not recognize the gradual loss. Chronic consequences from low-level exposures often circumvent a prime warning signal—pain. Exposure to sublethal levels of carbon monoxide can cause dizziness. As in the case of the acute carbon monoxide victim, the chronic victim is unable to detect the presence of odorless carbon monoxide or recognize his loss of acuity. The rise of carbon monoxide emissions in freeway and traffic congestion is emerging as principal concern of air pollution control efforts.

Variations in human susceptibility can further complicate full understanding of low-level exposures. Dr. Norman Ashenburg, University of Rochester School of Medicine, observed, in *Nursing Outlook,* "One cannot separate easily the biologic effects of specific air pollutants on man. . . . If the levels of the chemical are high enough, it is true that everyone exposed will suffer adverse effects. But at lower levels, individual host tolerance as well as many other factors may play a role in susceptibility. . . ." The aged, the young, the pregnant, the fetal, and the ailing (particularly cardiopulmonary patients and persons with inborn metabolic errors) are generally regarded as more susceptible to long-term exposures than normally healthy adults. However, as Dr. J. H. Schulte, Department of Preventive Medicine at the Ohio State University, observed before an Air Quality Criteria Symposium sponsored by the Department of Health, Education, and Welfare, the reverse can sometimes be true. Dr. Schulte pointed out that a person suffering from carbon monoxide poisoning can tolerate longer exposures to pure oxgyen than a healthy individual.

Thus, it may be seen that the comatose state or the limited oxygen carrying capacity of the blood (In the case of carbon monoxide poisoning) has a directly antagonistic or protective effect, if you will, against the toxic effects of oxygen under these conditions. There are many additional examples of disease states in which the individual is much more resistant to specific toxins than a healthy individual (e.g., the dosage of tranquilizers tolerated by agitated schizophrenics).

The many variables in low-level, long-term exposures can serve to defy the most modern methods of analysis. In contrast to chemical and organic compounds, radiation low-level exposures have received considerable study. Yet, as Dr. William L. Russell of the Atomic Energy Commission's Oak Ridge Laboratory, told a University of Vermont symposium on nuclear power, "There will never be absolutely accurate estimates of biological effects [of low-level radiation]. It's all guesswork, and we guess the best we can . . . We don't know all the risks."

Amid such scientific doubt, the risk-taking expands. Some 80 nuclear plants were under construction or ordered in the United States in 1969. When completed, all will be releasing low-level radiation. Construction workers are not the only persons continually exposed to asbestos dust. Over 3000 household products contain asbestos. DDT, the first man-made organic chemical used as a pesticide, was marketed in 1944. Today almost 500 insecticides, pesticides, herbicides, and fungicides incorporated into 54,000 formulations are registered for use in the United States. The lag between the introduction of these products into the environment and the knowledge of their potential health hazards has led to serious concern over whether preventative medical action can await incontrovertible evidence of danger. The Committee on Air Pollution for the American Thoracic Society has declared:

Universal agreement on the role of the several types of community air pollution in causing or aggravating conditions such as lung cancer, bronchitis and emphysema may require many decades, during which time additional millions of persons will continue to have significant exposures. The more prudent course should be to prevent pollution now whenever and wherever possible, rather than to run a substantial risk of damage to the health of the community while incontrovertible evidence of its dangers is accumulating.

Epidemiological studies play an important role in showing the way to reduce risks amid incomplete understanding. A committee member, Dr. John Goldsmith of California's Environmental Health Hazards Evaluation Unit, told a Congressional committee that, "It is not essential to understand the mechanisms by which the [epidemiological] associations occur as long as it is clearly demonstrated that the associations exist and that when the associations are weakened the undesirable health effects are also diminished."

Based on epidemiological studies relating respiratory stress to exposure to photochemical smog, Los Angeles area physicians advise up to 10,000 patients yearly to leave the Los Angeles area, according to the Los Angeles County Medical Association. The Association has also established a School Smog Warning Program, which prohibits physical fitness programs when certain air pollution levels are reached. Pupils affected number over 1.6 million; during a peak smog month (October), these pupils may forgo up to nine days of physical fitness and athletic programs. Such restrictions on human activity and residency promise to increase as exposure to potentially harmful waste products increases.

Waste pollution can raise psychological as well as medical problems. Continuous exposure to noise, besides affecting hearing, can induce fatigue, reduced efficiency, and nervousness in factory workers. Under noise attack, the human body is gripped by uncontrollable reactions, as described by New York ear specialist Samuel Rosen of Mt. Sinai School of Medicine before the 1969 meeting of the American Association for the Advancement of Science in Boston: "The blood vessels constrict, the skin pales, the pupils dilate, the eyes close, one winces, holds the breath, and the voluntary and involuntary muscles tense. Gastric secretion diminishes and the blood pressure increases. Adrenalin is suddenly injected into the bloodstream, which increases tension, nervousness, irritability, and anxiety." Besides the potential for hypertension, continuous noise attack may weaken blood vessels through repeated constriction and relaxation. Dr. Rosen observed, "The time will come when [blood vessel] recovery will not be rapid and the entire circulatory system will be damaged. You may forgive noise but your arteries never will."

In its ability to interrupt communication, forceably dominate the hearing senses, interrupt sleep, and induce fear, noise can also create stress and tension. After observing how sonic booms startle people, Dr. S. S. Stevens of Harvard's Psychophysics Laboratory suggested a possible "synergism" between a boom and a surgical operation: "The surgeon making a delicate incision will jump too. I hope I am not the patient on the table when the SST flies over."

Noise to one person may be music to another, as in the case of amplified rock-and-roll music. Noise may also perform a helpful "masking" effect, such as air conditioning units in thin-walled apartments and crashing surf on a crowded Sunday beach. To safeguard privacy in large offices, church confessionals or psychiatric treatments centers, "white noise" or "accoustical perfume" units that emit low-level masking noise may be installed.

The unwanted sound affects behavior and sensibilities adversely. Variations in human tolerance can make this phenomenon difficult to measure. Decibels alone are not a sufficient measurement; for example, a low hum may be undesirable in a musical recital. Transportation advances, however, especially in the form of jets and supersonic planes, are exposing more and more people to intermittent noise emissions that generate widespread complaints and jammed airport switchboards. The startle effect in noise that protects us from unseen hazards is being transformed into a psychic irritant. "Experiencing it [a sonic boom] is like living inside a drum beaten by an idiot at insane intervals," notes Dr. Garrett Hardin of the University of California at Santa Barbara.

Air pollution can deprive or insult the senses through reduced visibility, eye irritation, odors, and discoloration (such as the whiskey-brown color of photochemical smog). With the advent of acute air pollution disasters, a dirty airshed may be fear-inducing as well and raise the possibility of mass transportation panic as visibility diminishes.

Polluted waterways, too, can assault the senses with odors, discoloration, turbidity, and dead fish. Landscape littering—solid wastes, decomposition, spawning rats and flies—can generate human repulsion. The extent to which waste pollution can affect human behavior and sensibilities can be difficult to measure because of its subjective nature. Waste pollution does demonstrate an ability to repel or drive down human activity even though the level of pollution may not be physically hazardous to health. Property damage, to be discussed later, can result from this, particularly in the case of airplane noise. The most serious psychic impact of waste pollution may thus be its ability to restrict or deny the exercise of the human senses. The desire to escape the city periodically and see and sense a natural environment is very strong, as the congested national parks suggest. As global population and pollution increase, we may be forced to repress this compelling sensory drive.

Our ability to adapt to various natural environments raises the question of whether we can adapt to a polluted environment. On a mental level at least, we do show a capacity to adapt to pollution by virtue of our residency in that part of the environment most exposed to pollution—the large metropolis. This capacity stems from mental conditioning: the economic choice (or necessity) of suffering the consequences and risks of pollution for the benefits of material well-being. Our biological capacity to adapt is even more limited than our mental capacity. As epidemiological studies indicate, people will continue to reside in airsheds whose impact on health can be deleterious.

In reality, our ability to colonize so many different natural environments stems from expansion of our habitat technology, not expansion of our natural tolerances and stresses. Within plant species such as tobacco and pine, resistant strains to air pollution have been identified and isolated in order to breed pollution-resistant strains. But such genetic manipulation is no cure-all, even for plants. In Volume I of *Air Pollution,* C. Stafford Brandt and Walter W. Heck report, "Where breeding programs are initiated they must take into account the characteristics already bred into the varieties in general use, such as flavor, texture, growth habit, and insect and disease resistance, to name a few. Thus, a breeding program, once started, would be a major and costly effort. In addition, even the resistant varieties are injured as the concentration of pollutants is increased. With increased industrial and urban expansion, there is no leveling of pollution load in sight; thus, breeding programs are not in themselves sufficient." Moral questions aside, the ability to develop broad-scale, pollution-resistant strains, including man, is severely limited by many factors. Michigan State University botanist John Cantlon notes, "To think that we could breed resistance to any list of pollutants in any significant number of these species—even if we know what ones to select—is patently absurd."

Man's mental capacity to adapt to pollution may thus be seen as an additional threat to his health. By his readiness to live in a polluted environment, he can intensify his exposure to the acute, chronic, and psychological consequences of waste pollution.

the threats to property

Waste pollution can damage property as well as people. Polluted air serves to bathe our cities in a solution of solvents for many chemicals. With its corrosive mix of acid gases, oxidants, and hydrocarbons, an urban airshed can tarnish, erode, and fade our buildings and our clothes. Cities with high sulfur dioxide levels, such as Chicago and Philadelphia, literally tend to lose more weight because of materials corrosion than cities with low levels. Corrosion targets range from marble buildings to computers, which are being short-circuited by electric contacts smitten by polluted air. Smoke and tarry aerosols can blacken a building surface; acid gases can erode the surface. Air pollution can double or triple the rate of decay of stone in an urban area. Pollution cleaning can be costly, up to $10,000 for a 15-story building, but necessary. Buildings built to withstand earthquakes and hurricanes can still be gradually dissolved by urban air.

Air pollution investigators in Cincinnati recently concluded a day's work, only to find their cars had turned brown in the open parking lot. Vapors accidentally released from a chemical refinery accomplished this color change free of charge. High sulfur dioxide levels can transform paint exteriors on homes to a universal black.

Our artistic heritage is particularly susceptible to air pollution. The air of Athens is dissolving the friezes on the Parthenon while sulphurous fumes are dissolving the heads, the hands and the breasts of Venice's graceful statues. Inside as well as outside museums, white dust piles up at the base of horses sculpted centuries ago. "These statues have cancer," an art expert told a *Life* reporter. "Venice must become a hospital."

In 1843, Michael Faraday related the rotting of a leather chair in a London club to the London air. Leather gradually cracks and then disintegrates under the attack of sulfur dioxide fumes.

Ozone in photochemical smog can induce cracking in windshield wipers, tires, and other rubber products. Embarrassed young ladies have been told that their blouses and nylon stockings are disintegrating; natural and synthetic textile fibers can be weakened, soiled, and discolored by air pollution.

The corrosive effect of polluted air can be expensive as well as embarrassing. A Public Health Service study compared costs for outside and inside maintenance of houses, laundry, dry cleaning, and hair care in Steubenville, Ohio, and Uniontown, Pa. Per-capita annual costs were $84 higher in Steubenville, the principal difference attributable to Steubenville's higher level of air pollution.

Materials susceptibility to air pollution could play an increasingly important role in materials selection. Aluminum withstands air pollution significantly better than steel, and granite and certain sandstones are more resistant than limestone, marble, mortar, roofing slate, and other carbonate materials. Fortunately for people and animals who wear fur coats, animal fibers are generally more resistant than natural or synthetic textile fibers. (Ironically, the rapid obsolescence and one-use nature of an increasing number of products, from "disposables" to new-model cars, serves to ameliorate accelerated deterioration from air pollution.)

A column on gardening that appeared recently in the London *Times* asserted that plants were being protected from pests by the sulfurous nature of London air. Although this particular assertion may be true, fumigation by air pollution is more often associated with expensive damage to our crops and livestock. Besides dazing pests, air pollution can alter plant growth, injure leaves, and induce discoloration. Lettuce has been bronzed by smog and ethylene fumes have caused young bolls of cotton to drop. Plants with thin leaves are especially vulnerable, as farmers who grow grain, salad crops, spinach, grapes, and tobacco have discovered. Plants with fleshy leaves or needles—citrus, pine—are more resistant, although photochemical smog from Los Angeles has overcome this resistance. As chemist C. R. Thompson of the University of California at Riverside notes, citrus trees in ambient air conditions in southern California yield less fruit (sometimes less than half) than trees in carbon-filtered air. Increased leaf drop (up to 30 percent) is another characteristic of smog-exposed citrus trees. Sulfur oxide and fluoride effluents have devastated large areas of commercial forests. In the Copper Basin area of Tennessee, some 7000 acres of rich deciduous forest were denuded. Gully erosion ensued and the entire watershed was adversely affected. Fluoride emissions from a smelter burned pine needles and killed ponderosa pine over a 50-square-mile area near Spokane, Washington.

Fluoride emissions from the heavy-chemical industry can induce calcification of bone and tissue structures in livestock. Cows produce less milk, lose weight, and become crippled by overgrowth of bony spurs in the knees. Uptake and concentration of fluoride effluent in pastures grazed by the cows becomes the deadly agent of transmission. Chronic and acute lead poisoning has also been observed in farm animals grazing near lead smelters and mines.

In 1968 more than 6000 sheep grazing on the Utah desert plains died after exposure to nerve gas emissions accidentally released by an airplane involved in chemical and biological warfare research. The nerve gas poisoning cost the U.S. Army $371,685 in livestock damage claims as well as $198,300 for temporary loss of pasturage through contamination.

The California Department of Public Health estimates that air pollution losses to agronomic species in that state exceeds $100 million a year. Nationally, the losses are estimated at $500 million annually by the Department of Health, Education, and Welfare. Although impressive, these figures represent only those damages that can be documented, such as acute episodes. Chronic episodes are much harder to document, as in man, while carcinogenicity and mutagenicity remain beyond evaluation. Observes botanist Michael Treshow of the University of Utah, "Field studies have never considered the possible effect that air pollutants might have on such processes as photosynthesis, respiration, vigor, growth regulators, or reproduction. Also, what do we know about the influence of air pollutants on pollen viability, flower set, fruit and seed development, flower and fruit abscission, numbers of ovules forming seed, seed viability, and seedling survival?" In reality, economic studies are measuring the consequences of a handful of well-known contaminants, such as ozone, PAN, sulfurs, and CBW emissions that can be traced. In addition, losses from total abandonment of crops (such as spinach in the Los Angeles area) often escape measurement.

It was once noted that air pollution might help to stop cigarette smoking by eliminating tobacco crops. However, smog-resistant tobacco strains have been isolated and the Public Health Service is sponsoring research to develop smog-resitant pines. Land-use planning has been suggested as another means to reduce crop damage from air pollution. O. C. Taylor, horticulturist at the University of California's Air Pollution Research Center, has stated, "We may have to permit relatively high levels of pollution to exist in certain areas because of the industrial orientation of the economy. Plants sensitive to such levels would have to be grown elsewhere, or the grower would have to accept the risk involved." However, the broad toxicity and mobility of air pollution tend to counter rush-rush genetic manipulation and fugitive farming. The unemployed Los Angeles spinach grower could go 100 miles to the east and still be within the range of Los Angeles smog. By using the atmosphere as a dump, we are beginning to immobilize another function of our natural life-support system: food generation. Observes botanist Treshow, "While [agronomic losses from air pollution] represent a significant segment of the total economic loss ascribed to pathogens and toxic substances of all kinds, they may be minor when compared with the potential losses to the far greater acreage of nonagronomic forest and range vegetation constituting the natural ecosystems of the country."

Waterways used as dumps can also prove hazardous to property. The Corps of Engineers spends $2.8 million annually to clear telephone poles and other dumped navigational hazards from San Francisco Bay. If the waterway passes through a lumbering area, as the Columbia River does, navigation can be made especially risky by cast-off stumps, particularly at night. Litter on the seabed as well as the surface can jeopardize property. Recently a mining company decided to mine phosphate nodules off the southern California shore. The shocked company found the marine bank littered with bombs. The bank was used as a bombing range and dump by the Navy. Instead of armor-plating their equipment, the company decided to get a seabed lease refund from the Department of the Interior. A fishing vessel off North Carolina recently dredged up a bomb that detonated at the surface and killed the fishermen. The bomb had missed its mark during World War II submarine warfare. Such explosive debris promises to booby-trap glamorous and ambitious seabed exploitation projects. Oceanographic vessels are already snagging expensive trawling equipment on rocket engines, old refrigerators and other sunken debris.

Waterbound wastes that are neither solid nor explosive can harass property, as the scum rings on boat hulls in polluted harbors demonstrate. Periodic oil spills intensify these scum rings. A build-up of oily emissions can make water a fire hazard. Recently the Lower Cuyahoga River near Cleveland became inflamed and nearly incinerated two bridges. As we "conquer" the ocean with oil rigs and other proliferating forms of marine technology, we will undoubtedly encounter more property damage.

Noise pollution is even translated into property damage. Two public schools near Los Angeles International Airport have been closed by increased frequency and intensity of jet noise, which would often blot out 15 minutes of instruction time in an hour's period (see Figure 9). Soundproofing of classrooms was considered but re-

*the
dump
spills
over*

figure 9. *This Los Angeles public school was closed because of noise from incoming jets landing at nearby airport.*

jected because of the prospect of even higher noise levels. And soundproofing and acoustical perfume cannot protect physical education and other outdoor classes. Hospitals, outdoor musical stages, and residential areas can also be very noise-sensitive. Courts have recognized damage claims for jet noise on the basis that an easement has been taken without compensation. Some 589 residents living on the acoustical fringe of the Los Angeles International Airport have received $740,000 in court-awarded noise damages. (The City of Los Angeles, the airport landlord, is appealing the decision.) The easements and the damage claims that may result from future jet traffic are staggering. By 1975, noise levels from Los Angeles airport traffic at which a "vigorous response can be expected from the community" can be expected to affect at least 41 schools, five hospitals, and eight parks, according to a Department of Transportation study prepared by Bolt, Beranek and Newman, Inc., in 1967.

A new Ottawa air terminal building closed shortly after opening because of shattered windows and damaged roofs, walls, ceilings, and doorways. A sonic boom from a low-flying jet fighter effected the quick closure. The shock waves as well as decibels let loose by supersonic craft imbue the potential for property damage with a new dimension. Sonic booms have been held responsible by the National Park Service for shattering Indian caves and scenic cliffs in two parks in the Southwest. Aircraft vibration joins with corrosive air to help crumble the Parthenon. The sonic boom potential for triggering snow avalanches and burgler alarms is presently being investigated. (A chicken farmer charged that Air Force sonic booms inhibited egg-laying and triggered fatal chicken stampedes. The courts upheld his damage claims. In 1968 a federal court in Minnesota awarded $37,490 in damages to a mink farmer who claimed an Air Force boom triggered a stampede that killed 2,000 baby mink.) Although the Federal Aviation Agency estimates that the average boom from supersonic transports will be 1.5 pounds overpressure per square foot, booms of up to 120 pounds overpressure per square foot have been measured. Projected averages are of little assurance when two or three above average "slips" could send eardrums, skyscrapers, and cliffs vibrating. By using the landscape and our eardrums as a noise sink, we inbue our once-quiet life-support system with an increasingly formidable hazard to our health and our property.

the threats to natural resources

Waste pollution endangers another principal asset of our natural life-support system: natural resources. Severely polluted water can still flow in a river but provide no fish to catch and no water for drinking, irrigation, and industrial purposes. Waterfronts that are essentially off-limits to human use are a principal feature of urban environments. The Hudson River that flows past New York City could be a magnificent aquatic resource for 7 million urban residents . . . but it is polluted. Such urban waterways, reduced to industrial gutters, exist as a mere shadow of their natural prowess. New York City goes upriver and upstate for its drinking water and fresh-water fish, thereby intensifying pressures on limited aquatic resources.

Investment in water pre-treatment plants can salvage some of the values of a polluted river for drinking and industrial purposes. However, this pre-treatment does little for fish. As a result, the continued survival of fresh-water

the
dump
spills
over

and estuarine fish stocks is, at best, a question mark. The Federal Water Quality Control Administration estimates that 15 million fish, two-thirds of which had been classified as having commercial value, perished in fish kills in 1968. The largest kill, 4 million fish, occurred when a petroleum refinery released chemicals into the Allegheny River. Many years are necessary for fish to reestablish themselves to their former abundance after such devastation. Artificial restocking efforts can be frustrated by the continuing threat of water pollution: coho salmon introduced into Lake Michigan created a popular salmon fishery. However, the salmon is now considered unsafe to eat because DDT levels are above Public Health Service limits.

Fish kills are no longer much of a problem in Lake Erie, where continuing pollution pressures have largely reduced a rich fauna to sludge worms (up to 36,000 per square yard of lakebed). The use of such estuaries as Chesapeake Bay, San Francisco Bay and Tampa Bay as dumps imperils a significant statistic. Some two-thirds of our marine catch is estuary-dependent, either for spawning, feeding, or shelter. That many of our shellfish stocks are unsafe for consumption indicates how we are jeopardizing the life-giving values of estuaries. Many estuary-dependent waterfowl are being exposed to such hazards as lead poisoning by ingesting spent shot. By wholesale pollution of our estuarine system, we run the risk of sterilizing the offshore and the skies. Rising wasteloads thus hold the potential of rendering fish for food, commerce, and recreation a memory.

The fertility of soils can also be jeopardized by pollution. Mine and smelter wastes from surface mining can drain across the landscape and render pasturage and farm soil too toxic or acidic to support livestock, crops, or wildlife. The Department of Agriculture estimates that 2 billion acres has been despoiled by surface mining. (These mineral wastes can also contaminate groundwater.) Copper-mill tailings account for 40 percent of the total mineral waste problem; uranium mine tailings introduce a new soil threat: radiation contamination. At the same time, soil acidity can be intensified by raindrops that precipitate sulfur compounds from dirty airsheds.

*man
and his
environment:
waste*

Now that we have learned to exploit natural resources on such a wide scale, we find this prowess mocked by our wasteloads. This self-defeating anomaly becomes especially apparent in the field of outdoor recreation. While our productive power gives us increased leisure, our wasteloads deprive us of substantial opportunities to enjoy the gift of time. The Chicago lakefront contains 15 beaches, 15 parks, and many marinas, all within the shadow of smokestacks and skyscrapers. Yet such an inviting and valuable waterfront is a rarity in urban America. The Chicago lakefront is the only urban lakefront along the Great Lakes that is not periodically shut down by pollution. Of 62 beaches along Lake Erie, only three are rated safe for swimming. Offshore oil leaks and spills now hold the potential to periodically shut down oceanfront as well. All our leisure time, the power boats, the water skis, the Scuba tanks, and the fishing poles can thus be rendered useless by the wasteloads that affluence generates.

This boomerang from our style of material productivity promises to deny us the pleasures of national forests and parks. The metropolitan Los Angeles basin lies within the shadow of mountain ranges preserved as national forests. For the past 25 years, smog has been shrouding these mountains from view, but the 4 million urban residents are still able to drive up into the mountains to enjoy their forest charm. Recently, forest rangers have noticed an unusual number of pines with yellowing needles and excessive needle drop. The yellowing denotes ozone concentrations that break down chlorophyll processes and destroy a tree's food producing systems. The U.S. Forest Service now estimates that 1.3 million trees in the San Bernardino National Forest are being killed by smog and that death may come within five years. The weakened trees are more susceptible to the voracious pinebark beetle. Plant pathologist Robert Bega's requiem is simple: "These aren't lumber trees; they're people trees." We can set aside all the rivers, vallies, and forests that we want and still not be sure whether such high-minded conservation will be rendered repulsive by air, water, noise, and solids pollution.

the threat to survival

Once only a smelly nuisance, waste pollution has amply demonstrated its ability to harm our health, property, and natural resources. Its consequences can be merely irritating, like noise at a concert, or devastating, like floods, earthquakes, tidal waves, and other natural disasters. In fact, waste pollution is beginning to rival man's other great man-made disaster, war. More and more of our activities are influenced by its silent yet continuing presence, whether we fish, farm, or just breathe. We feel its impact in the middle of the city or the wilderness.

What we don't know about the impact of waste pollution is as foreboding as what we can ascertain. Unable to gauge fully the long-term and synergistic effects of our wastes, we still release new and untested compounds into the environment and place our health at the mercy of our ignorance.

By transforming our natural life-support system into an increasingly hostile environment, we place ourselves in an increasingly precarious position. We can no longer trust the purity of the air, the water, or the soil because of the extent of waste pollution. Defending ourselves against the dangers of this hostile environment is proving very costly, if not impossible. As waste discharges make the environment more hostile, new "records" in fish kills, forest kills, and smog kills can be expected until there are no more fish, forests or air-breathers left to kill. It would be ironic but not inconceivable if waste pollution reduced our ability to pollute by reducing our numbers and our resources.

The impact of man's development into the dominant species on the planet thus becomes apparent. The uncontrolled productivity and population growth that makes this possible also generates wasteloads that turn our life-support system more into a dangerous dump. This self-defeating cycle presents a choice: controlling our wasteloads or risking adaption to a hostile environment. Such a choice has drawn increasing public attention to the often-ignored field of waste treatment and control. The resulting view, more often than not, tends to intensify concern over our predicament.

*man
and his
environment:
waste*

SUGGESTED READINGS

American Association for the Advancement of Science, *Air Conservation,* Washington, D.C.: AAAS, 1965.

American Speech and Hearing Association, *Proceedings* of the June 13–14, 1968, National Conference on "Noise as a Public Health Hazard," cosponsored with HEW, Washington, D.C.: ASHA Reports, no. 4, 1969. *See also* Federal Council for Science, "Noise: Sound Without Value," September, 1968.

Food and Drug Administration, "Hermann Muller, FDA, and Chemical Mutagens," *FDA Papers,* Washington, D.C.: FDA, July–August, 1969.

Hanks, T. G., *Solid Waste–Disease Relationships,* Washington, D.C.: Department of Health, Education, and Welfare, 1967.

Kneese and Bower, *op. cit,* chap. 3. Reviews health, property, and natural resources damage from water pollution.

Lapp, Ralph, and Jack Schubert, *Radiation,* New York: Viking, 1957; Compass Books, 1958.

Miller, Paul, *Air Pollution and the Forests of California,* Riverside, Calif.: University of California Air Pollution Research Center, 1969. Center has available a number of papers on plant damage from air pollution, including ones by Dr. O. Clifton Taylor.

National Academy of Sciences, Committee on SST-Sonic Boom, *Human Responses to the Sonic Boom,* Washington, D.C.: NAS, June, 1968.

Senate Subcommittee on Air and Water Pollution. *Air Pollution—1968.* Congressional Hearings, Parts Two and Three, contain extensive material submitted by medical societies and experts, including Goldsmith, Cassell, and Epstein. *See also* Los Angeles County Air Pollution Control District, "School Smog Warning Fact Sheet," 1969.

Schurcliff, William, *S/S/T and Sonic Boom Handbook,* New York: Ballantine, 1970. Health, property, and natural resource damage.

Stern, *op. cit.,* pt. III, sects. 14 and 15.

Williams, Clara, "Drug-Pesticide Interaction," *FDA Papers,* Washington, D.C.: FDA, September, 1969.

5
trying to right the dump

the genesis of waste transfer
The gravity of waste pollution would suggest an appropriate program of waste control. Standards on emissions to protect life and property would be established. All potential waste emissions would be evaluated prior to general release. Emissions that could not be safely reprocessed and recycled would be prohibited or sharply controlled. Politically, waste management systems would transcend local political boundaries to reflect the regional mobility and impact of emissions. Waste generators would share in the financial support of such comprehensive management systems.

Waste management in reality is the direct opposite of this type of program. Traditional waste management has occurred at a local level, with little or no standards, and with the financial burden often on the victim of waste pollution. Within this local perspective, treatment of wastes has become almost synonymous with transmitting them downwind, downriver, and down the road. If this waste strategy does not reflect the true scope of the problem, it does reflect accurately man's traditional appreciation of the biosphere and his relationship to it.

Historically, waste control was first recognized as a local problem. Visible symptoms—smell and unsightliness—became regarded as the only consequences of waste pollution, and these consequences could be easily controlled at the local level. (That bad odors—"miasmas"—were considered carriers of disease added to the concern over putrefying smells.) Nomadic tribes would remove themselves rather than the trash when the stench became overpowering. As man forsook wandering for permanent settlement, garbage would be thrown out the tent flap or the window to be recycled by pigs and chickens. However, as wasteloads and smells spiraled, the control strategy shifted from waste recycling to waste transfer. The Greeks, the Romans, and the Egyptians would often cart their dung and their garbage outside the town gates and downwind. Even mythology was not above exploiting concepts of waste transfer. According to Bulfinch, "Augeas, King of Elis, had a herd of three thousand oxen, whose stalls had not been cleansed for thirty years. Hercules brought the rivers Alpheus and Peneus through them, and cleansed them thoroughly in one day." (Donald Nicoll, legislative assistant to Sen. Edmund Muskie, notes, "There is no record of what happened to the two streams, or to those who lived downstream from the stables.")

Waste control thus became keyed to waste transfer, the idea being to dispatch the wastes and the miasmas somewhere else. Waterways and airsheds were recruited for waste transfer; currents and winds could be depended on for transport. Chimneys poked up into the smoky sky and gutters and outfalls converged on redolent waterways; waste "treatment" became limited to expediting transport of the wastes into the appropriate natural dump. By the nineteenth century, the gutters had become so big and their contents so viscous that Charles Dickens could have had Fagin accidentally drop and lose his hard-won jewels into a London gutter. A standard credo—the solution to pollution is dilution—began to take hold.

Man was thus deliberately as well as unwittingly emitting wastes into the environment. In an age of wasteloads devoid of throwaway cans, pesticides, hydro-

trying to right the dump

carbons, and high BOD, this strategy had a certain logic. However, it also encouraged habits and attitudes that have proved hard to shake off. The environment as dump became regarded as an important and beneficial resource. Industries as well as cities could release bothersome wasteloads into the environment free of charge. If curtains were blackened by industrial smokestacks or commercial fish stocks expunged by urban outfalls, society at large accepted these discomforts as the necessary price of industrial and civic progress. In 1661, John Evelyn published an essay entitled "Fumifugium, or the Inconvenience of the Aer and Smoke of London Dissapated; together with Some Remedies Humbly Proposed." Evelyn's remedies included sharp restrictions and bans on a relatively new source of energy, the burning of coal. London was more willing to forgo this concept of waste prevention than the prospect of industrial progress, however grimy. Grime itself became a symbol of progress and achievement, as noted by the editor of *Environmental Science and Technology,* Dr. George Bower. The stench from industrial smokestacks was joyfully characterized as the "smell of money" by factory barons. An old Yorkshire saying proclaimed, "Where there's muck, there's brass."

Pollution acceptance and adaption thus complemented waste transfer. The natural environment itself existed as jumbo resource to be exploited at will, and human effort and knowledge revolved around resource exploitation.

In the nineteenth century, typhoid epidemics were related to drinking water infected by human feces, and waste pollution became regarded as a health hazard as well as nuisance. This linkup helped inspire the movement for public health and sanitary measures.

It is interesting to note that one of England's public health advocates, Edwin Chadwick, held to the miasma theory of disease and rejected Pasteur's germ findings. Chadwick in part personified an attitude that is reemerging again—that fouling the natural environment per se is bad.

Through the use of sanitary measures, communities set out to protect themselves from the health threats of contaminated water and putrefying garbage. This was accomplished less by controlling waste emissions then merely refining waste transfer concepts. The outfalls, smokestacks, and dumps became only longer, taller, or further away. Pollution acceptance was formalized, as evidenced by "No Swimming" and "No Fishing" signs on urban waterfronts. Collection of waste water and garbage became community-wide to expedite transfer. Mystery writers became blessed with a unique setting to secrete the Phantom of the Opera and other nefarious characters—underground storm and sewer drain systems —while the "honey" cart operators—the carriers of dung—evolved into million-dollar sanitary collection companies. Waste treatment beyond transfer was minimal. Underground sewer pipes might have passed through a central sewage treatment plant, but treatment became largely limited to filtering out objectionable solids prior to mass discharge into the nearest waterway. The plant was merely a gross screen. The "solution-to-pollution-is-dilution" credo remained intact.

The refined waste transfer system offered apparent public benefits in its simplicity. Few standards on waste emissions were needed, and public investment was limited to sewer works or dumping grounds. The concept of the environment as a cheap dump was maintained while generators of waste continued to get a free ride on the environment. Physical and human resources could remain concentrated on exploitation of the biosphere.

short on knowledge

Today waste pollution is recognized as much more than just the "smell of money." The platforms of both major political parties recognize waste pollution as a major national problem. The various pollutions have all qualified for their own governmental bureaus, and these bureaus busily foster standards, upgraded pollution control facilities and research in the waste pollution field. Where there's muck, there's liable to be a pollution inspector. Ambitious timetables have been set to cleanse the air and the water.

Society's traditional orientation toward resource exploitation, however, haunts all this late-blooming recognition. A rational system of waste control, by its very nature, must stem from a comprehensive knowledge of the stresses and tolerances of the natural environment. A waste's harmful traits—from toxicity to corrosion—must be identified, quantified, and related to a variety of potential receptors, from humans to car paint. Integrated into this picture must be the waste assimilative capacity of the receiving medium (or mediums, depending on the waste's mobility) and the potential for synergism. Environmental management in general, and waste management in particular, is thus more demanding of our knowledge than single-resource management. To design an auto, the knowledge of auto engineers is needed. To control air pollution, the knowledge of auto engineers, meteorologists, doctors, psychologists, agronomists, botanists, economists, and materials engineers is needed, and this knowledge must be synthesized in a form meaningful to policy-makers and the general public.

Yet ecology—the study of living organisms in relationship to the environment—and the concept of interdisciplinary studies are both in their relative infancy. Biologist René Dubos has observed, "The very word ecology was introduced into the scientific language only 100 years ago by Ernst Haeckel, the German biologist, so recent is the awareness that all components of nature are interwoven in a single pattern and that we too are part of the pattern!" The agency with the most knowledge, if any, of a waste's properties is often the waste generator. However, there are no profits to be made in divulging, much less controlling, the harmful effects of a product's waste after-life. Indeed, the opportunity to discharge freely and indiscriminately into the environment has been serving as a major means of cost reduction. Proprietary rights can often buttress a waste generator's reluctance to release environmental information on a particular product. In California, citizens cannot find out about the types and quantities of pesticides being used agriculturally because release of this knowledge might abuse proprietary rights. For the same reason, Santa Barbara city officials have been denied access to information about the offshore oil operations that threaten their beaches. "One wonders if the stamp 'proprietary' will come to be used in information dealing with civilian environmental prob-

lems the way 'secret' is used in the military domain,"
observes Los Angeles *Times* science writer Irving
Bengelsdorf.

Often a waste generator will be inclined to use his information power to discourage controls on his discharges. In contending that there are no known safe
levels for radiation discharges, the Minnesota Health Department has set power plant discharge levels that are
more stringent than those of the Atomic Energy Commission. In challenging the constitutionality of the state
requirements, the commission charges that states lack
appropriate expertise and that state standards could lead
to "total and utter chaos." This controversy is presently
before the courts.

Preoccupation with resource exploitation goals over
general environmental considerations can even carry
over into the university, whose research horizons are
often defined by government and industrial contracts. Dr.
Bengelsdorf of the Los Angeles *Times* has even observed, "Rachel Carson was wrong. It is not the spring
that is silent. It is the scientists and engineers—the one
element in our society that really knows what is happen-
ing in the pollution of our environment. The silence from
our universities has been deafening."

Because of such traditional attitudes, a waste may
generally be released into the environment without having its full harmful effects, if any, ascertained. A waste
must manifest its hazardous nature in the actual environment before attracting attention, much less control. In
the nineteenth century, reforms in waste disposal had to
await the advent of typhoid epidemics and this deadly
lag continues. Before a 1969 senate hearing on national
environmental policy, botanist Orie Loucks of the University of Wisconsin observed:

*We were distressed in the late 1940s to see the rapid
movement of DDT from the forest or lawn litter, to
earthworms, and then to birds, but we were prepared
to accept these modest upsets for the increased crop
production, forest protection, and physical comfort
afforded by DDT. It was nearly 15 years before the
apparent disappearance of DDT from a treated area was*

*demonstrated to be due, not to the breakdown of DDT,
but due to its transport into the atmosphere attached
to evaporating water. . . . Only in the last two years
have the mechanisms of population decline [in
top-carnivore birds exposed to DDT residues] become
identified, and they are somewhat different for each
group of animals affected. . . . In addition, and perhaps of more consequence, is the fact that DDT and
its breakdown products act to stimulate breakdown in
some of our modern wonder drugs in the body before
the drugs have an opportunity to act. . . . Our two
decades of controlling insect pests with DDT has
produced a wave whose impact now threatens to be
greater than any of the upsets it was designed to
correct.*

Because of such a time lag, the modest residues of a
relatively nondegradable waste like DDT can build up to
harmful levels before the need for control is recognized.
A global ban on DDT use could be enacted today and its
harmful side-effects would still be with us. It is also noteworthy that the complex unraveling of DDT's side-effects
came less from responsible government, industrial, and
university groups than from individual researchers and
conservation groups like Audubon Society. Consciously
or unconsciously, society too often places protection of
the living environment on just such a volunteer, *ad hoc*
basis. Dr. Loucks now notes that introduction of herbicides in Wisconsin corn fields coincides with mass
mortality of marsh cattail in adjacent wetlands.

*Was there anyone that could test for the presence of
herbicides [in the wetlands]? The State Department of
Natural Resources said that this would be very
technical and that the University would have to do it.
The University staff in the area said that it would take
up to two years to develop suitable techniques for
sensing the very low concentrations of herbicides
involved. Thus, without proof that there is a herbicide
problem we could not justify a budget for monitoring
of materials that are capable of damaging much of our
wetland vegetation. Without a budget, we cannot get*

*even preliminary evidence for or against the potential
hazard of herbicides in wetland waters.*

This wholesale lack of preliminary evidence severely undercuts an essential first step in comprehensive waste control—standards on waste emissions. The federal government, in cooperation with states, is now establishing standards on emissions into waterways and regional urban airsheds. (It is likely that such standard-making will be extended to noise levels in the environment in the near future.) Yet, although thousands of wastes are daily being emitted into the environment, standards for only a relative few exist because of lack of evidence. For instance, standards on air emissions are often restricted to those which have received initial research attention: sulfurs, nitrates of oxide, carbon monoxide. The setting of standards on a few individual emissions fails to recognize the wide variety of emissions as well as the potential for synergism.

Given the imprecise nature of standards knowledge, influences other than scientific ones come into play. Lack of knowledge suggests the need for rather strict standards tending toward natural or ambient levels in the environment. Although such conservative standards might fail to utilize the environment's full waste-receiving capacity and thus incur high treatment costs, they would serve to reduce the known (and unknown) hazards of waste pollution. The strict approach, however, imposes higher treatment costs on industry and municipalities, the agencies that have traditionally used the environment as a dump. Because standards are often initiated at the local level, local economic impact of standards can override the larger social impact of waste pollution. The Federal Water Quality Control Administration has asked states to refrain from polluting any waterways in a pristine state. However, 31 states have refused to accept this nondegradable standard in order to reserve the right to pollute in the interests of future industrial and domestic discharge needs. Through such an economic prism, a large metropolis may give greater weight to the costs of upgrading waste discharge standards than to the impact of these discharges on downwind or downriver communi-

*trying
to right
the dump*

ties. Los Angeles, for instance, is noted for having the nation's strictest air emission standards and yet even these standards are not sufficient for downwind agricultural and resort communities. Palm Springs is a desert resort noted for "clean, desert air." However, smog generated by Los Angeles is sufficient to spread over 2600-foot passes and envelop the desert havens of refugees from Los Angeles smog. The nomadic approach to pollution, as well as the dilution approach, fails. "This is just like a loaded gun pointed right at the heart of Palm Springs," notes Palm Springs's city attorney. "Our life blood is clean air." (Air pollution expert A. J. Haagen-Smit recently looked up at the Palm Springs sky and remarked casually to his hosts that he might as well be in Los Angeles.) Through such a local perspective, standards can easily lose sight of the regional impact of waste pollution, including highly mobile wastes like DDT, and the wide variety of exposed receptors, from wilderness trees to marine fishes.

Sometimes a city or state will seek strict waste standards but be overruled at the federal level because the standards affect a federal waste generator like the Atomic Energy Commission or the Federal Aviation Agency.

Economic determinism can thus serve to modify the protection that waste standards are intended to foster. Instead of reflecting comprehensive pollution control, a set of waste standards may reflect the level of pollution a community or area is willing to accept and risk—even if the odds are not known.

short on success

Once enacted, waste standards must be implemented. The process of implementation often serves to further emasculate the standards. The technical "state of the art" of waste control well reflects society's traditional appreciation of such matters. "We do not fight, communicate, build, or educate as the Romans did, but our smouldering dumps are very much like theirs," observes industrial economist Arsen Darnay in a report for HEW on solid wastes. The traditional emphasis, if not fixation, on waste transfer has served not only to thwart new innovations but to rule out strategies such as waste reuse and waste prevention.

This technical backwardness can be compounded by organization. Most waste management agencies are restricted to only one aspect of waste pollution, be it air, water, solids, or noise. This type of fragmentation hardly reflects the ability of wastes to change form and commute between the air, the water, and the soil. Even at the federal level, waste pollution is compartmentalized into the Federal Water Quality Control Administration (Department of the Interior), Bureau of Solid Wastes (HEW), noise abatement (Department of Transportation), and National Air Pollution Control Center (HEW). Thus waste management is fragmented along structural as well as political lines. This type of dual fragmentation often serves to put the waste generator effectively beyond the control of the waste victim. A city council may condone waste water discharges that pollute downstream neighbors and at the same time submit unsuccessful pleas to the Federal Aviation Agency to reduce jet noises overhead. A presidential proposal to consolidate federal-level pollution control agencies into an Environmental Protection Agency (EPA) was approved late 1970.

The imposition of new waste standards on such a waste management system can be traumatic. Generally the standards require upgrading of existing waste treatment facilities. As mentioned before, one reaction is to upgrade the waste transfer system—make the outfalls longer, the smokestacks taller, and the dumps more distant. This sort of response has already generated the world's tallest smokestack: A 1200-foot smokestack in West Virginia is designed to send power plant emissions above the surrounding residential hillsides. The smokestack has an aircraft warning beacon. (Plans to use it as a tourist attraction fell through.) Ocean outfalls off southern California measure up to 10 feet in diameter and extend out as far as 7 miles (see Figure 10). High-level liquid radioactive wastes are being buried underground in huge concrete tanks lined with steel. These tanks must be built to last as long as the radioactive life of the wastes, which can approach thousands of years. *Environment* editor Sheldon Novick, author of *The Careless Atom*

*trying
to right
the dump*

figure 10. *The diameter of ocean outfalls races to keep abreast of urban wastewater loads.*

observes, "These atomic burial grounds are the most costly tombs since the days of the Pharaohs."

The rising volume of wasteloads and the limits of building technology make the resort to elongated waste transfer increasingly unfeasible. The heat of radioactive decay keeps liquid radioactive wastes boiling, and this nuclear broth has exposed some storage tanks to temperatures beyond design control limits. In 1968 the Atomic Energy Commission requested $2.5 million to replace failed or failing atomic tanks in Richland, Washington.

Because of their sheer size, elongated systems are prone to overlap with other human activities; smokestacks in the smog-smitten Los Angeles area have been limited to 500 feet because of flight-safety considerations.

Elongated waste transfer systems are also liable to bump into each other as neighboring cities contend for dump space in the air, water, and land. Chicago, for instance, managed to protect its lakefront by breaching a small drainage divide and diverting its sewage wasteloads to downstate rivers. This waste transfer system was officially recognized as one of the civil engineering wonders of the world. This diversion, however, served to pollute the aquatic resources of downriver communities as well as to lower water levels in the Great Lakes and to foster lawsuits by neighboring states and Canada for endangering navigation.

The limitations of waste transfer have encouraged forms of pretreatment before release of wastes into the environment. Thus, in wastewater treatment, secondary treatment may be added to general (or screening) treatment. Secondary treatment exposes sewage effluent to filtering and decomposition action that significantly lowers the BOD level. Smokestacks, auto exhausts and jet engine housings have been refined and improved to reduce air and noise emissions. Solid wastes may be incinerated or buried by sanitary fill. The Atomic Energy Commission is trying to reduce liquid radioactive wastes to solid form for storage in abandoned salt mines, but technical factors have yet to be resolved.

Such waste treatment is far from complete. Organic wastes in sewage effluent that go through secondary treatment are transformed into the residual waste products that can enrich and age waterways. Relatively nondegradable substances, such as pesticides, mineral salts, and synthetic "hard" detergents, escape secondary treatment unscathed. Higher burning temperatures in air discharge equipment can reduce hydrocarbons and sulfur emissions but increase emissions of oxides of nitrogen, essential to formation of photochemical smog. A random survey of 6000 dump sites by HEW found that only 6 percent of the dumps were truly sanitary in operation and procedure. Even those dumps labeled as sanitary fill generated flies and methane fumes because of incomplete or faulty earth fill. Such faulty fill procedures can nullify a principal goal of sanitary fill: reuse of the land. Unexpected subsidence and methane fumes strong enough to asphyxiate humans can even deter recreational use. A person who parked his car in one parking lot returned to find his car at the bottom of a cavity 30 feet deep. The parking lot was built on a dump not properly compacted. The car was retrieved by a crane. To be on the safe side, building contractors may drive steel support pilings through the dump to bedrock, only to have the pilings be corroded and weakened by decomposing organic acids and gases. Sometimes the pilings may not be able to reach bedrock because concrete rubble and junk autos are in the way.

The Atomic Energy Commission has found out that its atomic burial ground in Hanford, Washington lies within an area of moderate earthquake activity. The tanks were not built to withstand earthquakes.

Because of the incomplete nature of treatment, rising wasteloads can serve to counter temporary gains made by pretreatment of wastes. This incomplete nature can also foster situations in which one agency's waste disposal becomes another agency's waste pollution. Bay tidelands and mudflats are often recruited as sites for sanitary fill (see Figure 11). But tides can leach out pollu-

figure 11. *Spoil from dredging project is used to reclaim fertile marshlands as real estate. Such reclamation often shrinks a bay's tidal prism and intensifies water pollution problems.*

tants from the fill site. At the same time, marine and bird life lose a valuable habitat. Shore reclamation through fill also restricts the bay's tidal prism and reduces its waste-assimilative capacity. That one waste agency can thus solve its problems only by increasing the problems of another waste agency is logical in a management system fragmented on political and structural lines.

Incineration of solid wastes can contribute significantly to air pollution if not controlled. Because of this, backyard incinerators were banned in Los Angeles, and this ban promptly increased the wasteload burden of the city's refuse system.

The tribulations of the Rocky Mountain Arsenal illustrate well the ability of wastes to subvert conventional waste control. The arsenal near Denver produces chemical warfare agents and a large liquid chemical wasteload. These wastes were traditionally disposed of by shunting them to evaporation ponds. However, as Rachel Carson noted in *Silent Spring,* these holding ponds became chemical laboratories that spontaneously generated chemical poisons that seeped into local groundwater and contaminated shallow wellwater in an area 6½ square miles in size. "Crops were dying, the water was unpotable for humans and apparently injurious to livestock. Property values dropped from $500 per acre to $250," reported geologist David Evans of the Colorado School of Mines.

The arsenal began looking around for alternate means of waste disposal. Chemical and industrial trade journals heralded a relatively new alternative: "Throw Your Wastes Down a Well . . . Good Riddance . . . You've Got It Lost . . . Nobody will ever see it again and you can hold your head high—ask your friendly geologist." These reviews referred to deep-well injection: the disposal of liquid wastes by pumping them into suitable subsurface stratum. Such a concept is particularly tantalizing to firms handling toxic wastewaters that are hard to treat. Soon the arsenal was injecting 300 gallons of wastewater per minute 12,024 feet below the surface of the earth at a maximum injection pressure of 550 pounds. A month after injection operations commenced, Denver experienced its first earthquake in 80 years. From April, 1962,

*trying
to right
the dump*
to September, 1965, 710 earthquakes were recorded with epicenters in the vicinity of the arsenal (see Figure 12). As many as 20 tremors a day were recorded.

The earthquake magnitudes were relatively minor, ranging from 0.7 to 4.3 on the Richter scale. Geologist Evans suggested that underground pressures generated by the injection program were causing underground stresses that were shaking the earth. Investigations by the U.S. Geological Survey, the Army Corps of Engineers, and the Colorado School of Mines agreed that a relationship existed between the injection program and the earthquakes. Also, the pattern of earthquake epicenters extending northwest from the well suggested that the earthquakes originated from rock movement in a northwest–southeast fault or fracture zone. The well was shut down February 20, 1966. "Since then, the arsenal

figure 12. *Map of earthquake epicenters for September, 1968, Rocky Mountain Arsenal.*

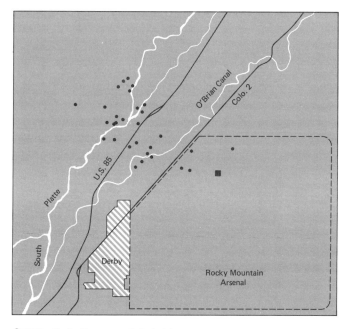

Source: D. B. Hoover and J. A. Dietrich, "Seismic Activity During the 1968 Test Pumping at the Rocky Mountain Arsenal Disposal Well," U.S. Geological Survey circ. no. 613, 1969.

disposal program has been completely revamped. Now, no disposal ponds or wells are needed," observed Evans in an address to the American Association for the Advancement of Science entitled "Industrial Disposal Wells —Solution or More Pollution?" The disposal well that cost the arsenal—and U.S. taxpayers—$1.5 million is closed.

The arsenal managed to make waste headlines once more in 1969 with plans to ship millions of tons of aging gas bombs across the continent for disposal off the New Jersey shore. The risk of transcontinental shipping and the possibility of the bombs disintegrating in the corrosive sea solution and releasing toxic gases drew congressional protests. The arsenal is now rendering the bombs chemically inert on the plant grounds on the advice of the National Academy of Sciences.

The waste problems of the arsenal suggest that awareness of environmental side-effects is just as critical in waste management as resource exploitation . . . and just as liable to be ignored. A recent editorial in the August, 1968 issue of *Mechanical Engineering* declared:

More than any others, engineers know what can be accomplished with current technology—and what remains beyond its reach. Full application of that professional knowledge will avoid much false hope and many abortive efforts to accomplish what we simply do not yet have the means to do."

In the same magazine, an article ("Deep Down Waste Disposal") lauded deep-well injection with no reference to the Rocky Mountain Arsenal or other instructive examples. Frank Conselman, former president of the American Association of Petroleum Geologists, has linked oilfield brine injection in Texas to contamination of several water wells and to salt springs suddenly sprouting in dry creekbed bottoms. Deep-down disposal, unencumbered by the "full application of professional knowledge," can thus imbue wastes with another harmful trait: pressure.

A recent rash of bear attacks on humans in national parks has given rise to demands that bear populations, particularly grizzlies, be sharply restricted or even purged. A *Sports Illustrated* cover depicted a toothy, salivating bear with the caption "Bear or Man?" This starkly posed confrontation stems in part from another indiscriminate form of waste disposal. Park refuse and garbage is often dumped out in the open and bears come to feast. These bear feasts rival geysers and waterfalls as a visitor attraction. Up to 1000 persons have crowded and shoved to get a front-row view of bears feeding in a garbage pit just outside Yellowstone National Park. Yet such "attractions" help promote the confrontations between bears and humans that often end in tragedy. If the garbage is buried, the bears often dig it up. If the dump is closed, bears may forage in garbage cans in inhabited areas. By weaning bears on our garbage dumps, we create a situation that benefits neither us nor the bears in the long run.

A waste control system that diligently upgrades its facilities to meet standards and avoid spillover pollution can still have such commendable efforts severely jeopardized. Most control agencies, because of inherent economic and political limitations, can control only a portion of the waste sources necessary for effective control. Many wastewater sanitary districts separate storm drains and sewage drains; a combined system tends to overload treatment facilities during storms and force release of raw sewage. (Residents who lift up manhole covers to expedite storm drainage are the bane of sanitary engineers.) However, storm drains can discharge into a city's waterway street refuse and accumulated organic material with a considerable shock pollution load. Adequate waterway protection must include comprehensive litter control and street cleaning programs, programs over which a sewer district often has little or no control. At the same time, many municipalities are either unable or unwilling to convert to separate sewer-storm drain systems, and their combined systems continue to habitually pour out raw sewage during storms. The 59 million people who live in communities served by a combined drain system continually experience sewage overflows and back-up flooding, often in their own basements.

Irrigation runoff, soil erosion and mine drainage are other waste sources that may be beyond effective control. These sources, being diverse and often rural in location, defy pipeline collection for central treatment. Control at the source, particularly for soil erosion, is most feasible but means to effect this have been limited. Soil conservation efforts have largely been aimed at farmland. Yet cull lands, abandoned farmland, and highway and suburban construction can be principal sources of silt loads. Old mines contribute to acid mine drainage, but many of these mines are abandoned and no responsible party exists. Such uncontrolled sources can effectively keep a waterway polluted and counter improvement efforts.

The condition of San Diego Bay in California has been greatly enhanced by upgrading of standards on waste discharges and improvement of municipal and industrial treatment facilities. Sludge deposits accumulated over the years—some 7 feet in thickness—are finally beginning to decompose as the bay regains its self-purifying ability. The San Diego Regional Water Quality Board, a state agency established to control discharges, has spearheaded this cleanup drive. Raw sewage has continued, however, to gush into the bay from a source beyond the effective control of the board, the U.S. Navy. Since up to one-fourth of the active American fleet can be anchored in the bay, indiscriminate ship discharges can jeopardize the ambitious and expensive cleanup efforts. That the Navy is a part of that level of government, the federal government, which has been requiring local waste agencies like the Board to upgrade water quality would seem to bode well for efforts to toilet-train the Navy. Yet the Navy, like so many other waste generators, has tended to resist controls over its discharges. Only after considerable prodding from the Federal Water Quality Control Administration has the Navy begun to control its discharges into San Diego Bay and other bays throughout the United Staes.

The Navy also runs a firefighting school in the San Diego area. For 25 years, this school has been discharging enormous clouds of sooty smoke that make the worst single stationary source of air pollution in southern California. Once more, local officials find themselves powerless to enforce anti-pollution regulations on a federal facility. Former President Lyndon Johnson issued an executive order requiring all federal agencies to conform with local pollution regulations. Unfortunately this order, like so many directives on waste pollution, failed to recognize that waste pollution control costs money. Congress waited until 1969 to appropriate the $1.3 million needed to control southern California's worst stationary source of air pollution.

Inglewood, California's model noise ordinance control covers emissions from dragsters, motorcycles, amplified musical instruments, and almost everything except the chief noise source—the jet flight patterns overhead that lead to Los Angeles International Airport. These patterns are regulated by the Federal Aviation Agency. Like the Navy, the FAA tends to regard consideration of environmental side-effects as being subordinate to its traditional regulatory functions. Through such limited perspectives, the federal government finds itself in the position of adding to pollution problems while attempting to control them. Washington attorney Harold Green has observed, "While the Secretary of Health, Education, and Welfare dons his armor and mounts his white charger to purify the environment, his colleagues, carrying out what are presumably equally important programs, are polluting and planning to pollute the environment."

Sometimes the various levels of government can overcome fragmentation of waste management and come up with a fairly unified position. Offshore oil leaks and spills have led to national and even international agreements designed to prohibit such emissions in offshore waters. But offshore oil spills continue to wash into harbors and beaches. The need to lighten an oil tanker's load by pumping out dirty bilge water can take precedence over international regulations in the eyes of a tanker captain. The risk of being caught is lessened by the fact that offshore oil spills can be difficult to identify and trace to a particular source. Thus waste discharges, even when prohibited by law, can be beyond control when detection and enforcement is hard. As mobile sources of noise, air, and water emissions expand, the detection problem promises to expand.

Stationary sources of oil spills and leaks, such as

reef-trapped oil tankers or offshore oil wells, do not escape detection easily; the problem here is treating the oil once it escapes. Recently, television viewers were treated to the sight of thousands of men pitching straw on the southern California shore. Such a large congregation of men engaged in such a menial task seemed more appropriate to the frontier days of the United States than to the present age of automation and machines. That the straw was being pitched on a beach instead of a farm field added another incongruous note. And yet when the discharge from the Union Oil blowout in the Santa Barbara Channel covered 800 square miles of ocean and 30 miles of beach, the most advanced nation in the world was reduced to soaking up the oil with straw pitchforked by prison trustees and the National Guard. Massive accidental discharges from other large-scale technological efforts, such as nuclear plants, promise to be just as difficult to control. Recently, beaches in the Newport Beach area of southern California were quarantined for four months. Winter floods destroyed inland sewage treatment facilities, and millions of gallons of raw sewage gushed down a riverbed to pollute inshore waters. Ironically, the quarantine was in effect at the same time that the National Guard was pitching oil-soaked straw in the Santa Barbara area. If the oil and sewage spills had occurred in the summer instead of the winter, a season of surfing, sunbathing, and tourism would have been eliminated on substantial portions of southern California's shoreline.

Los Angeles's frustrating struggle with air pollution illustrates well the ability of the waste pollution problem to transcend waste control efforts. The regulations of the Los Angeles County Air Pollution District govern smoke, nuisance, particulate matter, sulfur compounds, combustion contaminants, dusts and fumes, open fires, gasoline loading, and animal reduction processes. Controls have been applied to such diverse sources as incinerators, rendering cookers, coffee roasters, petroleum refineries, chemical plants, rock crushers, asphalt plants, crematories, and dog food production. The district's engineering program has devised new control innovations in precipitators, baghouses, fume burners, centrifugal collectors,

*trying
to right
the dump*

scrubbers, absorbers, and adsorbers. Through such extensive programs, the district has sharply reduced air pollutants from industrial, domestic and other stationary sources. Yet despite all this effort smog levels remain relatively constant in Los Angeles. Up to 70 percent of the air pollution comes from a mobile source, the auto. The ability of a local waste control agency to tell an entire industry how to design pollution-free products is both technically and politically limited. Controls on auto emissions (now being attempted at state and federal levels) are encountering a major technical obstacle: the ability of the internal combustion engine to meet stringent standards. The ultimate solution may be to switch to a pollution-low power plant, such as steam or electric. Yet this strategy of waste prevention would run counter to industry's traditional prerogative to design products exclusively on market considerations. Thus a city's ability to solve a major pollution problem may depend less on its own efforts than national efforts to resolve major social and technical issues. A report by the School of Public Health at the University of California at Berkeley notes, "Air pollution control seems to be a gigantic game of trial and error—witness, in Los Angeles, the initial emphasis on control of sulfur dioxide emissions from refineries, followed by prohibition of backyard burning, followed by installation of blowby and motor exhaust devices, and now the interdiction of reactive hydrocarbons. Each step has helped but an acceptable solution seems as far away as ever."

short on economics

The shortcomings of conventional waste control demonstrate the critical need for large-scale financial investments to bring all waste sources under effective control. Logic would have the waste generators who have been passing on pollution costs to society in general bearing a substantial portion of the control costs. The quest for economic equity, however, suffers from another legacy of the waste transfer system. As Allen Kneese and Blair Bower note in *Managing Water Quality: Economics, Technology, Institutions:*

*A distinctive feature of the modern problem of water
quality is the fact that the economic institutions on
which we customarily rely to balance costs and
returns—the interaction of market forces in a
private enterprise system—do not perform this
function satisfactorily for waste disposal. In deciding
how to dispose of its wastes, an upstream firm or city
is not forced to take into account the costs imposed
by its effluent discharge upon downstream water users
or the value of other uses of the water that may be
foreclosed by its action.*

Costs that cannot be "internalized" by the market system
are commonly called "diseconomies." Kneese and Bower
observe, "Water pollution and air pollution are economists' classic illustrations of the theoretical concept they
refer to as "technological external diseconomies.'"
Both large corporations and individual citizens are prone
to heed this concept. In his contemporary novel *Bullet
Park,* author John Cheever describes how city residents
shifted their waste problems to the owner of a spacious
suburban estate:

*At the edge of his property was a sign that said:
"No dumping. $50 fine. Violators will be prosecuted."
Below the sign was a gutted automobile, three defunct
television sets and a soiled mattress . . . The night
population of Bullet Park was sparse but its most
inscrutable and mysterious members were the
scavengers' opposite—the dumpers . . . It was
cheaper and easier to drive especially to Bullet Park
from the city and dump your waste than to have some
professional haul it away.*

Appeals to civic responsibility, e.g., "Clean Air Week,"
"Don't Be a Litterbug," have been invoked to encourage
waste generators to reduce wasteloads. If the costs of
waste reduction are low, a waste generator may find himself in a position to heed these appeals. If the costs are
high or business slow, a waste generator may feel he
cannot afford civic responsibility. The downwind or downstream victims of such economic analysis may go to

court to seek damages and encourage a broader view of waste control investment. However, adversary proceedings can be costly and lengthy, and provide only immediate relief and damage remuneration. Often, a pollution victim may be unable to identify who to sue or enjoin. For the homeowner whose exterior paint job is soiled by urban air or for the commercial fisherman whose ocean catch is contaminated with pesticides, there is nobody to sue.

Effluent standards backed up by enforcement provisions are used to encourage investment in waste reduction and control. Ostensibly, the imposition of effluent standards on a particular waterway or airshed would serve to reduce discharges to an acceptable level. The uniform application of effluent standards fails, however, to recognize the wasteload differences between various waste generators. A waste generator whose effluent discharges can be reduced at relatively low cost may find compliance quite feasible. Once he has complied, he has no further incentive to reduce his wasteloads further. A waste generator with a very heavy wasteload may find compliance much more difficult. He may even be forced to shut down or move, whereas another firm that could afford to reduce its wasteload does not because it has achieved the uniform standard. At the same time, a new firm or municipality that builds a new discharge facility has the advantage of tailoring construction to the standards and the latest control technology. In practice, effluent standards by themselves are only effective in reducing gross forms of pollution.

The federal government has provided financial grants to municipalities and industrial firms to help make compliance financially feasible. State governments have employed rapid tax write-offs and tax credits to encourage waste control investment. These financial incentives have helped to spur new treatment construction throughout the country and have helped upgrade—at least temporarily—some waterways, most notably the Ohio and Delaware Rivers. However, the choice to use or ignore these financial incentives is still determined in large part within the economic framework of each individual waste generator. The resulting variation in motivation is reflected in the case of Lake Erie. In 1968, Cleveland voters approved, by a 2–1 margin, a $100 million bond issue that, along with federal grants, will give the city one of the nation's best metropolitan sewage systems and provide citizens with a chance to regain use of their Lake Erie waterfront. However, the Federal Water Quality Control Administration estimates that a $1 billion program will be required to upgrade sewage treatment around the Lake Erie littoral and has set up a timetable of proposed investment and improvement. As of July, 1969, improvement schedules were being met by only 15 of the 102 cities and 32 of the 100 major industrial polluters. Cleveland's ambitious sewer system could be in vain; the effluent may be cleaner than the lake water into which it is discharged.

A recent report by the General Accounting Office found that $5.4 billion has been invested in sewage treatment facilities since 1957, with the federal government contributing $1.2 billion. In a study of eight waterways, the GAO found that such investment is effectively countered by continued outpourings of industrial waste. Along a stretch of Oregon's Willamette River, intergovernmental agencies expended $2.1 million to reduce municipal pollution by 20,000 units on a test scale. At the same time, two paper mills have been dumping between .5 and 2 million units into the same area of the river. Six Louisiana cities along the Mississippi River have expended $7.7 million in federal grants to reduce pollution by 147,000 units, but 80 industrial plants are putting 2.4 million units into the same river area. The GAO found similar countervailing forces along the Nashua River and Ten Mile River in Massachusetts, the Tualatin River in Oregon, the Pearl River between Louisiana and Mississippi, and the Saco River and Presque Isle Stream in Maine.

Sometimes an industrial polluter, to comply with effluent standards, civic appeals, and perhaps a lawsuit, will hook his sewage wasteload into the local municipal plant for treatment. However, the hydraulic loadings of industry can be such that the existing or proposed capacity of the municipal plant can be quickly exceeded. It seems fair that a municipal treatment plant should charge for its services on the basis of individual waste-

trying to right the dump load volume. Yet, under the traditional waste transfer system, the municipal plant must treat all dischargers as equals, from the fellow who flushes his toilet to the plant that flushes its industrial wasteload.

Besides contending with industrial wasteloads (in-plant or in-stream), municipal waste agencies find that they must make amends for another haunting legacy from the waste transfer days, the ill-paid, ill-recognized "sanitation" worker. As Mr. Harold Keoenig of the Ecological Science Corporation observed before a Congressional hearing on environmental quality:

Remember, operating and maintaining these unglamorous waste disposal, sewage plants, water plants, is a very, very fundamental problem today. Nobody likes to pick up other people's refuse. Nobody likes to work in stinky environments, and people, if they are hungry enough, will do it for a period of time, but after working all day in a stinking environment, handling stinking refuse, the guy himself begins to stink, and at some point in time it gets to him, and it is no wonder to us that we are seeing turmoil and expect one heck of a lot more turmoil among our garbage collectors across the country . . . Human beings now are saying, "If we have to do this unglamorous, dirty work, dirty hands work, we have to get paid more for it."

The environment has not been alone in subsidizing society's traditional disdain for waste control. An HEW survey performed by Aerojet-General Corporation found that sanitation workers have the highest accident frequency rate of any occupation, 4½ times higher than coal mining. Investigators do not know if this stems from the hazardous nature of wastes, the lower literacy of workers, or both.

Traditional economic constraints on waste control are beginning to exact a substantial toll. The federal government, in the passion of newly passed legislation on water quality standards and grants, has established a national goal of clean water by 1973. The Federal Water Quality Control Administration estimated that between $26 billion and $29 billion would have to be spent between 1969 and 1973 to attain this goal. In 1969, the FWQCA reported that municipal investments were running at less than half the amount necessary to reach the five-year goal. The municipal level is not alone in lagging behind goal attainment. The 1966 Clean Water Restoration Act authorized the federal government to spend $450 million on federal grants in fiscal 1968. Only $203 million was appropriated. Some $700 million was authorized in fiscal 1969, and $214 was appropriated. Some $1 billion was authorized in fiscal 1970 and the executive branch requested $214 million. (A strong Congressional effort succeeded in raising this to $800 million.) While seeking compliance with water quality standards, the federal government stints on its announced financial contributions.

The federal government could reverse itself and greatly increase its financial contributions, but this switch might be neither desirable or feasible. As Kneese and Bower observe:

*The concept of paying a waste discharger for reducing
the costs he imposes upon others is contrary to
the popular concept of fairness—even if such a
practice would assure greater economic efficiency.
In addition, there would be the task of raising
substantial funds through increased taxation. With so
many urgent demands being placed upon government
and the difficulty of framing taxes which themselves
do not distort resources use, there are serious
problems in obtaining the amounts required.*

Regulatory standards combined with enforcement and incentive grants can thus fall short of "internalizing" waste control costs in an effective and equitable manner. Downstream and downwind residents still remain vulnerable to the market decisions of upstream waste generators. "A society that allows waste dischargers to neglect the offsite costs of waste disposal will not only devote too few resources to the treatment of waste but will also produce too much waste in view of the damage it causes," note Bower and Kneese. Using the environment as a dump continues to be cheaper than large-scale waste reduction, wast recycling, and waste prevention. Manufacturers who produce pollution-prone consumer products appear to have an ideal mechanism to absorb pollution control costs—the consumer. Traditional market considerations once more emerge to overcome environmental considerations. The container industry, for instance, generates a large solids wasteload. A firm that tries to make its container more amenable to waste reduction may price itself out of existence. A plastics container firm must not only compete with other plastics firms but also with cardboard, glass, and metal container firms. To remain competitive, glass container firms have gone from returnable bottles to throwaway bottles, which advances company profits and consumer convenience at the expense of solids waste reduction.

Preoccupation with immediate market considerations can drive a deep and distressing wedge between a waste generator and a waste victim. In 1953, after photochemical smog was linked to automotive emissions, Los Angeles County Supervisor Kenneth Hahn asked car makers what they were doing to eliminate this link. A Ford official replied, "The Ford engineering staff, although mindful that automobile engines produce exhaust gases, feels these waste vapors are dissipated in the atmosphere quickly and do not present an air-pollution problem . . . The fine automotive power plants which modern-day engineers design do not 'smoke.' " Five years and many smog alerts later, after Los Angeles's extensive restrictions on stationary pollution sources removed any doubt concerning the auto's guilt, a Ford official wrote to Hahn: "We appreciate the role you have played in acquainting us with the Los Angeles smog problem. You also know that the automobile industry has taken cognizance of your problem and has done a yeoman job of research and engineering in order to speed to the Los Angeles area some type of device which you and your air pollution control district can accept as a means for reducing air pollution from automobile exhaust." However, actual accomplishments suggested that Detroit's recognition of the magnitude of the problem was limited at best. In

1963 Supervisor Hahn was still waiting for his control device: "Your company [General Motors] has done much to improve the performance and appearance of its products with one notable exception. Despite the great advancements in styling and horsepower, the smog-forming capability of the exhaust of your 1963 models is the same or more than the 1953 products."

Instead of writing letters to Detroit seeking voluntary control efforts, Hahn started writing letters to Washington seeking control through compulsory standards. Another variation on the waste generator-waste victim conflict occurred. Detroit, apprehensive about complying with many different state standards, urged uniform exhaust emission standards. California, apprehensive about uniform standards not being strict enough, urged that states he allowed to set stricter standards if they wanted to. This skirmish took on an added economic ramification when a Congressman playing a key role in the auto legislation expressed the concern that if states could set their own standards, "we'd have to run a separate [production] line for every place in the country." The Congressman's use of "we" was not accidental; he was from Detroit. The final legislation allows a state to adopt stricter standards with the approval of the HEW Secretary.

Application of compulsory standards now indicates that a new automotive power plant may be needed to meet emission standards of the future. The economic conflict that surfaced in 1953 now finds a new battleground: a company's traditional prerogative to control product design.

Seventeen years after Hahn wrote his initial request, Los Angeles and Detroit still remain estranged over the cure for photochemical smog. Interestingly, the "Big Four" auto makers, in sharp contrast to the many firms in the container industry, enjoy a very strong competitive position. There were no other auto makers to woo away consumers if the four auto makers each decided to increase car prices and research investments in behalf of an early and more aggressive effort to effect pollution control. But the traditional preoccupation with immediate *trying to right the dump* market considerations once more overcame timely consideration of environmental side-effects. In fact, the Justice Department filed an antitrust suit in 1968 against the auto makers on the charge of conspiring to *delay* development of control devices. The suit was settled out of court, with the auto makers signing a consent decree prohibiting them from conspiring to delay such development. (Los Angeles County is seeking to quash the out-of-court settlement in order to gain access to the sealed Justice transcripts and bring suit itself.)

The opportunity to sharply diminish, if not eliminate, one major form of pollution by effecting control over just one major source rarely occurs. Control of auto emissions would accomplish this in air pollution; yet traditional constraints on waste control put this opportunity out of reach. Thus material progress becomes synonymous with increasing waste pollution. This inevitability fosters increased reliance on pollution adaption and increased resistence to this consequence of conventional waste control.

SUGGESTED READINGS

WASTE MANAGEMENT—GENERAL

Aerojet-General Corporation, *California Waste Management Study: A Report to the California Department of Public Health,* Azusa, Calif.: Aerojet-General, 1965, chaps. 2 and 3 (distributed through Document Section, State of California Printing Plant, Sacramento). Excellent critique of the shortcomings of fragmented waste management.

Stewart, George, *Not So Rich as You Think,* Boston: Houghton Mifflin, 1968.

WASTE MANAGEMENT—SPECIFIC AREAS

American Public Works Association, "Water Pollution Aspects of Urban Runoff," report prepared for and distributed by Federal Water Quality Control Administration, 1969. *See also* "How San Diego Cleaned Up Its Bay," *Ocean Industry,* July, 1969.

Curtis, Richard, and Elizabeth Hogan, *Perils of the Peaceful Atom,* New York: Doubleday, 1969, chap. 10; Ballantine paperback, 1970.

Department of Health, Education, and Welfare, "The National Solid Wastes Survey," report prepared by Bureau of Solid Wastes, 1968. *See also* George Sowers, "Foundation Problems in Sanitary Landfills," *Journal of Sanitary Engineering,* February, 1968.

Evans, David, "The Denver Area Earthquakes and the Rocky Mountain Arsenal Disposal Well," *The Mountain Geologist,* vol. 3, no. 1, 1966. *See also* U.S. Geological Survey, "Seismic Activity During the 1968 Test Pumping at the Rocky Mountain Arsenal Disposal Well," circ. no. 613, 1969.

Loucks, Orie, "National Environmental Policy," hearings before the Senate Committee on Interior and Insular Affairs, 1969, pp. 169–172. Reviews pesticide and herbicide emissions.

ECONOMICS

Department of Health, Education, and Welfare, "The Cost of Clean Water and Its Economic Impact," report by the FWQCA, 1969.

Hahn, Kenneth, *Correspondence Between Kenneth Hahn, Los Angeles County Supervisor, and Presidents of General Motors, Ford, and Chrysler,* Los Angeles: 1967.

Kneese and Bower, *op. cit.,* chap. 5.

Murphy, Earl Finbar, *Governing Nature,* Chicago: Quadrangle Books, 1967, chaps. 6, 8.

6
pollution: adaption or control?

"As long as there is water in the Sea of Azov there will be fish," a Russian fishery minister said recently in evaluating the threat of water pollution. This innocent faith in the environment as a bottomless dump is no longer given much credence, even by waste generators. The rationale for pollution adaption in an age of smog alerts and quarantined lakes has found a different emphasis. Recently a continuing advertisement in the Los Angeles *Times* featured a man with a flashlight peering out of a dark background. The caption read, "A blackout in southern California?" The ad copy said that the recent New York power blackout stemmed from facility construction delays caused by government pollution regulations. Air pollution regulations in southern California were now serving to prevent expansion of three power plants because power plant discharge of nitrates of oxide is second only to autos. Warned the ad, sponsored by the prospective plant builder —Southern California Edison, "Could a widespread blackout happen here? Not likely now—but it could happen in the future if we don't build more generating plants now, as well as substations and transmission lines."

Pollution acceptance as a necessary

price of material progress is also cultivated by other industries faced with pollution restrictions.

If you want an instant end to air pollution . . . stop driving your car, then turn off your oil burner, brick up your fireplace, bundle your leaves, box your trash, refuse delivery of anything by truck, boycott airplanes, trains, buses, and cabs. Don't use anything which requires oil, gas, coal, or atomic energy in its manufacture—such as electricity, steel, cement, clothes, food, newspaper, babies' rattles and on and on and on and on . . . or let's face the fact that any combustion generates pollutants . . . and that any "instant end" to air pollution brakes our civilization to a halt.

This ad was sponsored by the National Coal Association. Sometimes the veneer of concern over pollution can slip in the heat of material concern. Congressman Craig Hosmer, an impassioned advocate of nuclear power plant expansion, has observed, "If the people of this country are going to have their demands for power met, they are going to have to accommodate themselves . . . They are going to have their electricity and they are going to shut up about ecologic conditions."

The prospect of tax dollars is also utilized to heighten pollution acceptance. "A new Edison plant can benefit your community in many ways, including millions of tax dollars every year to aid your local school districts. In fact, Edison is the largest single taxpayer in many of the communities and counties where we operate generating plants," notes Southern California Edison.

While conceding that their activities contribute to waste pollution, waste generators tend to minimize these contributions. The sheer scope of existing pollution may sometimes be employed to justify relatively new forms of pollution. "A conservationist is a guy who wants to make sure the 40 billion gallons of raw sewage going into Lake Erie each year contains no DDT," noted one pesticides industry magazine. Uncertainty over potential pollution effects may also be invoked to minimize pollution concern. AEC Chairman Glenn Seaborg has warned against "hysteria over thermal pollution" stemming from "maximum feasible misunderstanding." Seaborg notes, "While it is known that water temperatures and variations in those temperatures do have effects on aquatic life and its ecology and should be a factor in the siting of all thermal power plants . . . we still have a lot to learn about such effects." Alleged beneficial effects of pollution may also be invoked. Thus thermal pollution and sewage pollution may become "thermal enrichment" and "organic enrichment" in the semantics of waste generators. Responding to charges that ocean outfall discharges may adversely enrich the existing ecology, a Los Angeles outfall designer conceded that "we may be fertilizing the waters."

The risks involved in potential low-level or high-level radioactive emissions from nuclear power plants proves especially challenging to would-be semantists. "Radiation enrichment," for instance, wouldn't strike a very responsive chord. In *Perils of the Peaceful Atom*, authors Richard Curtis and Elizabeth Hogan quote Hal Stroube, an official with Pacific Gas & Electric Co., on the challenge of the atomic lexicon from a public relations viewpoint:

I would add that the time has come for some semantic soul-searching about the need for eliminating some other objectionable words from the atomic lexicon. Words such as "criticality"— "poison curtains"—"nuclear excursions"—"scram"— "maximum credible accident"—spring immediately to my mind, and I could list a dozen others if given time. . . .

Curtis and Hogan then quote an alternative semantic approach, as proffered by one conferee at a 1963 Symposium on Radiation Accidents and Emergencies in Medicine, Research, and Industry held in Chicago:

A second approach might be to consider radiation as being like a more powerful form of sunlight. While sunlight is not really a tangible phenomenon (and it is far from simple or fully understood), it is very familiar and benign. With this approach, biological radiation effects can be seen as something like sunburn (which is not too far off): a phenomenon which is familiar, is tangible, and is viewed as basically good, though dangerous when overdone. . . .

Advocates of pollution adaption may often offer up their employees as a test of environmental faith. "Nobody wants smog, including us," says Southern California Edison. "After all, 11,000 of us work at Edison. Our families live in southern California, too." The National Coal Association remarks, "Coal is a minor cause of this [air] contamination, but the coal industry is working hard to clean the air. After all, we're breathing it, too."

Such appeals for pollution acceptance can be consolidated into actual campaigns for pollution adaption. In a report entitled *Aircraft Noise and Community Relations,* the Federal Aviation Agency tells airport operators, "You must create acceptance by airport neighbors of certain irreducible noise levels caused by aircraft operations when they want these operations to cease entirely." The FAA report counsels the airport operator to establish an airport Noise Abatement Committee and then initiate interviews with radio and TV newscasters. The report provides a sample radio and TV interview format.

Airport Operator: The FAA considers noise control second only to safety. . . .

Announcer: I didn't realize that anything really could be done to reduce aircraft noise!

Airport Operator: Well, it isn't easy, but we can and are reducing it in a number of ways. Of course, we must all be realistic and recognize that the jet airliners will never be as silent as the horse and buggy. However, we do feel that the cooperative noise reduction programs now under way, both by the government and industry, are slowly reducing aircraft noise annoyance toward a level which the public will be able to accept as they have the noise of automobiles and railroad trains.

pollution: adaption or control?

With jet noise related to the progress of material welfare, the airport operator is advised to ennumerate the benefits of jet noise tolerance. A sample press release form reads, "These new jets have put [city] on the aviation map of the world and will greatly stimulate local travel and benefit local welfare and economy, [name] added." Noise tolerance out of patriotism can also be encouraged. "The sound of our own aircraft engines can be as reassuring to us as they were to the people of West Germany during the Berlin airlift," notes a companion FAA report on jet noise, *Sounds of the Twentieth Century.* "We must never lose sight of the importance of civil aviation to our national defense."

To communicate these appeals to "receivers" of noise, the FAA suggests a community speaker's bureau. "Pilots wearing their uniforms are particularly effective and helpful as speakers." When a new aircraft comes into service, a publicized test flight is suggested. "It [the aircraft] should arrive and depart at an announced time so that the entire community will have an opportunity to judge for themselves what the noise factor will be. In this regard, it will be extremely important that the aircraft's approach and departure be accomplished in a manner which will not create an unfavorable impression." At the same time, the FAA cautions against an overzealous approach to noise tolerance campaigns: "DO NOT try noise problems in the press. Unless forced to do so, never try for equal space to reply to attacks. Noise stories at their best are negative, so avoid at all times the cardinal sin of press relations, the spreading of a bad story."

Noise tolerance campaigns can be easily updated to meet new demands in noise tolerance. "Sonic booms are like a lot of things that get exaggerated when there is no information," commented FAA supersonic official Col. Robert Stephens. "People will get used to sonic booms. It will be just like a train passing their homes." FAA researcher J. H. Wiggins suggested a possible beneficial effect of sonic booms: "The booms slow down deterioration and aging of homes," he told a meeting of the Institute of Environmental Science. Based on government-sponsored sonic boom tests in New Mexico, Wiggins claimed that repeated sonic booms had actually lowered the rate at which structural defects show up in houses and other buildings. He suggested that the shaking a house receives in a sonic boom relieves accumulated stress. He emphasized that sonic booms with an apparently beneficial effect are of low level.

At times, waste victims may find pollution adaption as economically attractive or necessary as waste generators. Donora, Pennsylvania, for instance, resisted an aggressive crackdown on its chief air pollution source, the steel industry, even *after* the acute air pollution disaster. Explained local newspaper editor Harry Pore in a radio interview with Los Angeles station KLAC, "For almost since its founding right after the turn of the century, Donora lived of, by, and for its big steel mill. In fact, the community, you might say, was established because of the steel mill. This was bread and butter, it was the local economy, it was everything. The industry had a great deal to say about political life of the community. So that I think there was some understandable reluctance on the part of everybody to speak ill of the steel plant." Through such an economic prism, the main community problem becomes not pollution per se but the person who speaks ill of community pollution. Criticizing vocal anti-oil citizen groups in Santa Barbara for keeping the oil pollution issue alive, a motel owner with a surfeit of vacancies told a Los Angeles *Times* reporter, "It's the publicity that hurt us most." Commented the Chamber of Commerce director, "We are trying to overcome the idea that we are a disaster area. We'd like to see oil go quietly." Rebuffed by cities concerned about possible radioactive emissions, Boston Edison selected a depressed community, Plymouth, Massachusetts, as a site for a nuclear power site. "The town is sort of down on its uppers; it's sort of poor," an Edison official told a *National Observer* reporter. "When we announced it, they said, 'Oh, Santa Claus came.' They are better kind of people to deal with than you'll find in some of the metropolitan areas."

While becoming increasingly elaborate, pollution adaption campaigns encounter increasing resistance. The airport noise abatement committees, for instance, often intensify adverse public opinion as the intent to reduce noise complaints rather than noise becomes apparent. Nor does continued exposure to a form of pollution necessarily breed acceptance. In sonic boom test flights over Oklahoma City, the FAA found that noise complaints remained relatively steady during the duration of the flights. The material progress and affluence that pollution adaption programs seek to protect can serve to defeat such programs. Affluence tends to relieve people of extreme concern over economic survival, as in Donora, and heightens appreciation of aesthetic surroundings. Airline ads, for instance, boast of the quality of quiet *within* airplanes. That these ads may run alongside pleas to a community to tolerate overhead jet noise doesn't engender the forbearing mind that pollution adaption requires. Such an anomaly serves to impress on waste pollution victims the inequity of conventional waste control: waste generators consider control practical only when direct economic benefits can be gained. The "pollution may be beneficial" approach can also arouse considerable public skepticism. That low-level sonic booms may gently massage out structural stress hardly seems to balance out the risk of one accidental high-level boom that may shatter natural landmarks and urban windows. Such beneficial public gifts appear to stem less from a conscious program of public service than unconscious spillover from cheap waste disposal. This quality in thermal, organic, and structural "enrichment" tends to reassert how far removed waste disposal decisions can be from the persons most affected.

The willingness of people to accept pollution is also diminished by recognition of the fact that such willingness can prove very costly, if not suicidal. When photochemical smog first began to shroud Los Angeles, adaption appeared only to involve a willingness to forgo views of Catalina Island and the mountains and to suffer smarting eyes. At this point, smog fit well into the traditional view of pollution as a nuisance to be tolerated in behalf of progress. Then spinach crops began ebbing, young secretaries in synthetic blouses found themselves performing impromptu strip-teases, and car owners found their rubber wipers and tires cracking. Sixty miles away, citrus ranchers complained that Los Angeles's "filthy" air was damaging their orange trees. Pollution adaption now involved acceptance of economic damage. A University of Southern California medical team reported that athletic performance diminished in direct correlation with the intensity of smog levels. Los Angeles, noted for an all-year climate so conducive to outdoor sports activity, found such a natural advantage curtailed by auto exhausts. By 1969, pollution adaption involved curtailment of school physical fitness programs at certain specified levels of air pollution. (A football coach half-facetiously told environmental writer Frank Graham how he prepared his team for contests in Los Angeles: "First, we practice with one nostril taped, then we have an assistant coach smoke a big cigar in the bus on the way to the stadium.") Patients with respiratory and lung ailments were advised by doctors to leave Los Angeles because of possible complications from smog. The nuisance was now a medical hazard of unknown dimensions.

That Los Angeles's greatest period of growth parallels the advent of smog might seem to suggest the success of pollution acceptance. However, as the public has become aware of the full implications of such acceptance, resistance has increased. In the early 1950s, Supervisor Kenneth Hahn addressed polite pleas to auto manufacturers, Bob Hope cracked smog jokes and backyard incinerators were banned. By 1969, a state senator, Nicholas Petris of Oakland, was introducing a bill to outlaw the internal combustion engine by 1975. "We are living in an envelope of poison," declared Senator Petris. Initially the lobbyist for the Motor Car Dealers Association ignored the bill. "I thought it was a nutty bill," explained Kent Redwine to Los Angeles *Times* reporter Robert Fairbanks. The bill elicited surprising support and Redwine invoked the proven talisman: "This bill would stop the economy in this state so fast it isn't even funny." Despite this admonition, the State Senate passed the bill. It was finally defeated in the State Assembly. Senator Petris is reintroducing the bill. A state that joked about smog two decades ago is now seriously considering banning the basis of its two-door garages and eight-lane freeways—the automobile driven by the internal combustion engine. (The Petris Bill permits autos with steam, electric, or other pollution-low power plants.) Because of such formidable economic and medical risks, pollution adaption is losing its strict economic appeal, as well as appeals based on material comfort, patriotism and school tax dollars. At the same time that Donora was suffering the sulfurous belching of its smelters, another Pennsylvania city was debating a pioneer clampdown on air polluters. Despite an opposition slogan of "Remember Little Joe" (the average citizen who would ostensibly bear the burden of pollution regulations), the move for controls was approved by the voters. In October, 1948, as the people of Donora endured their pollution crisis, Pittsburgh was in the process of imposing pollution regulations that could have spared Donora the price of pollution acceptance.

pollution protection systems

Because pollution adaption now raises clear questions of biological as well as mental adaption, its supporters have been compelled to come up with other appeals. "If flies can build up resistance to DDT, why can't I?" was the rhetorical question raised by a California State Grange official opposing a DDT ban. The genetic approach to pollution adaption, beside being unsound, does not exude the ingredients of a very popular appeal. As *Environment* noted, "Uncounted millions of flies over many generations died of DDT poisoning before resistant strains of the insect developed." Based on the relatively short span of a generation of flies, thousands of years would be necessary for man to attain genetic resistance to DDT—even if this were biologically possible.

Pollution adaption through evolution of artificial life-support systems forms another attempt to reduce biological risks. Such an attempt is already in evidence: soundproofing of airport-area buildings and homes, pretreatment of drinking water, development of pollution-resistant food and fiber crops, smog-resistant building exteriors, and air filtration systems in greenhouses and orange groves. Tokyo, considered to have the world's filthiest air (some 34 tons of soot fall monthly per square kilometer compared with New York's 17 tons), has been a leader in attempting to pioneer pollution protection systems. Traffic policemen are provided with oxygen inhalators and school children must wear gauze masks. According to *Newsweek,* the man in the street has access to oxygen-vending machines in coffee shops arcades.

The health officer for Monterey County, California, recommends that residents immunize themselves against typhoid fever and hepatitis because of pollution of the county's seacoast. Much of this spectacularly scenic coast is in quarantine because of inadequately treated sewage discharges. "It's a shame that kids making sand castles on the beach might get typhoid. But it's a possibility now," Lloyd Austin, a University of California marine biologist and diving control officer, told a San Francisco *Chronicle* reporter. Austin's diving students must receive typhoid and hepatitis shots before checking on marine life in the Monterey area.

Pollution protection comports with the tradition of placing the costs of pollution control on the victim rather than the generator. With a ready-made market of waste pollution victims, business has been quick to exploit pollution protection. A cosmetics ad proclaims, "Perhaps the most important event in cosmetic history is the introduction of cosmetics that take into consideration all of the skin-aging environmental problems around you . . . A natural protective skin barrier known technically as pH acts as a shield between your skin and the polluted environment surrounding you." Above the ad copy beams a woman with the caption, "Of course I worry about environmental pollution." She is applying moisturizing cream to her face. During Los Angeles smog alerts, ads for Murine promise relief from eye-smarting ozone. Another advertisement depicts an urban scene of belching smokestacks with the caption "What's so fresh about outside air?" The ad continues:

It's about time we stopped talking about outside air as being "fresh." Air pollution in most of our urban and industrial areas is so great you can introduce more problems than you solve by bringing in 25% or 35%

*outside air. The day may come when building codes
read,"... no more than × % outside air" rather than
"... no less than." Air brought in through particulate
then activated charcoal filters is delivered clean and
odorless—fresher than any outside air.*

The ad was placed by a maker of activated charcoal, Barneby-Cheney. With an extremely porous structure (one pound of activated charcoal has over six million square feet of surface), activated charcoal has exceptional filtering abilities. During World War I, the Army made activated charcoal out of apricot pits to place in gas masks to ward off mustard gas attacks. Today activated charcoal is being used to trap the diverse ingredients of air pollution. Besides trapping hydrocarbons, ozones, and vapors, activated charcoal can filter out the smell of air pollution. (One pound can adsorb all of the pungent odor emitted when dozens of onions are peeled or the odor from 64 dram bottles of perfume.) Office buildings, homeowners with respiratory problems, and hospitals have found such virtues in activated charcoal filter units especially attractive. "The use of the carbon filter has been observed clinically to be of significant value in treating the patient with severe emphysema who suffers superimposed infection and bronchial obstruction in the presence of smog," concluded a University of Southern California medical study. "The adverse effect of smog as demonstrated in this study provides a rational basis for the use of carbon filters and justifies the expense." Another Barneby-Cheney ad proclaims, "Here's One Los Angeles Hospital That Doesn't Worry About Smog." The pollution protection potential does not stop with smog. The Barneby-Cheney fallout shelter filter "removes all radioactive dust and biological warfare agents ... poison gases and lethal vapors from chemical warfare, fire and ruptured gas mains."

While able to stem onion and smog attacks, pollution protection is not foolproof. Even activated charcoal cannot trap carbon monoxide and carbon dioxide. Pollution protection systems can suffer from serious nontechnical defects. Protection from pollution can become a matter of who can afford it rather than who needs it. Air filtration units, for instance, can be expensive. To be fully effective, they need to be coupled with an air conditioning system and electrostatic precipitators for particulate matter. In downtown Los Angeles, prosperous waste generators like Signal Oil Company and the Department of Water and Power (17 power plants) can afford "conditioned air" while their residential neighbors must make due with not-so-fresh outside air. Even in Tokyo, the oxygen-vending machines place a price on pollution protection—25 cents.

Given the increasing scope of waste pollution, artificial living systems would have to acoustically perfume, soundproof, airproof, and waterproof entire cities as well as buildings. In other words, artificial living systems would have to have the ultimate ability to replace natural life-support systems, including the atmosphere. In the interim, pollution disaster control would have to complement pollution protection. The Newark Bay–Bayonne Harbor Pollution Abatement Committee in New Jersey holds periodic simulated *Torrey Canyon* exercises to prepare for oil spills. (In 1968 the Committee was almost put to the test. A fuel barge loaded with more than two million gallons of oil struck a submerged object at the mouth of the Passaic River. "Had the barge broken open the pollution might have been on a scale never before seen in New York," reported the Port of New York *Newsletter*.)

Pollution disaster control can not only stagger port authorities but insurance companies (see Table 3). Tanker or drilling insurance against oil spills is available, but often with a $2 million deductable. Insurance liability is generally based on negligence, but the nature of modern pollution risks may require absolute rather than negligent liability, as indicated in the following exchange in a congressional hearing:

Senator Edmund Muskie (D-Maine): It strikes me to be a rather unusual situation when the owner of shore property who finds himself inundated from the sea by the results of an oil spill is told he must prove negligence against the unseen perpetrator or the originator of the

table 3

tanker oil spills, data on cleanup costs

vessel	date	location	product	amount in barrels	approximate cleanup cost
Torrey Canyon	1967	Scilly Isles, England	Crude oil	990,000 [a]	$7,200,000 [b]
Tank Countess	1968	Stavanger, Norway	do	1,500	60,000
General Colocotronis	1968	Bahamas	Fuel oil	120,000	800,000 [c]
Ocean Eagle	1968	Puerto Rico	Crude oil	71,400	700,000
Esso Essen	1968	Off Capetown, South Africa	do	75,000	200,000
Andron	1968	do	do	75,000	250,000
Sevilla	1968	do	do	3,000	— [d]

[a] Approximate total cargo on board.

[b] Includes some third-party damage claims.

[c] Includes cost of standby tugs and vessels used in removing oil from tanker.

[d] Oil dissipated by wind and currents and went out to sea.

Source: American Petroleum Institute.

spill in order to get damages under this kind of insurance policy, it seems to me that the nature of the problem of proof is so unusual as to suggest some different definition of liability than the one that runs through Anglo-Saxon law with respect to the normal kinds of risks.

Mr. Peter Miller (British insurance official): I may misunderstand the question, sir, but I beg leave to differ, it is unusual. If I walk out of this building and step in front of a taxicab and it is proved I was in a daze (which might not be surprising), and the taxi driver's brakes were excellent and indeed it was entirely my own fault, I would not be able to claim against the taxi driver.

Senator Muskie: It is hard for me to imagine a dazed beach.

Mr. Miller: That is quite true, sir.

Because of the potential scope of radioactive hazards involved, insurance companies will provide only limited liability insurance to atomic power plants, and the federal government must even help underwrite these limited policies.

A reader of the Los Angeles Air Pollution Control District regulations might feel justified in concluding that the district is prepared for a severe photochemical smog situation if it materializes: "Should a Second Alert stage be reached, with the advice of the Emergency Action Committee, the Control Officer may then order all industries contributing to the contaminant which caused the alert, to close down, and may stop all vehicular traffic, except authorized emergency vehicles." The district also has available an information sheet, "℞ For Heavy Smog Attacks," prepared by the Los Angeles County Medical Association. "Severe respiratory cripples living in smoggy areas should have facilities available for more intensive treatment," reads step F.

To see how such pollution disaster measures would be implemented, I went to the Los Angeles City Police Department. After requesting information on the traffic shutdown provision, I shuttled back and forth between four departments. No department head knew of any such

pollution: adaption or control?

plans. None was even aware of the provision to shut down traffic. "I've been here 16 years and this is the first I've heard about this," replied one officer. Another officer commented, "To freeze five million cars would be difficult, to say the least. The police force drives 200 cars. Are we supposed to stop, too?" Another officer snorted, "Everybody thinks that their particular needs should take priority over everything else." When I was finally referred to a department called Tactical Operations Planning Group, I thought I might finally be headed in the right direction. A quizzical look came over the face of the officer who greeted me after I told him what I wanted to know. "Well, actually, we're set up for riot control," he finally said. He did, however, comment on the shutdown provision: "It seems to me that if people want to leave the scene, particularly those most susceptible to air pollution, they should be allowed to. Why keep them here?"

During the Donora air disaster, the fire department dispensed between 250,000 and 300,000 cubic feet of oxygen. Because of a shortage of inhalators, people covered their heads with sheets and cylinders of oxygen were opened beneath the sheets. No plan for providing inhalator services for use during a severe pollution episode exists in Los Angeles. One inhalator unit per company is the proposed standard and there are 107 fire companies. Given the population of Los Angeles, the city is even less prepared for an air pollution disaster than Donora was two decades ago. To be effectively prepared, each large building should have, along with its fire extinguisher system, an inhalator system. Dr. Hurley Motley, a Los Angeles physician active in air pollution control efforts, has suggested that buildings with air filtration systems, such as the Department of Water and Power building and the oil company skyscrapers, be identified as possible "conditioned air" sanctuaries. As yet, no such identification has been undertaken.

The Donora experience demonstrated the difficulty of maintaining even minimal civic services. Rudolph Schwerha, the undertaker, coped with reduced visibility, as he explained in an interview with Los Angeles radio station KLAC.

From that traffic light about a mile and a half down, this workman of mine walked in front of me along the white line all the way down and all the way up on the hill because you couldn't see nothing, and I just followed him with my hearse, just followed him. I passed the house going up, I couldn't see it, and coming back down we passed it again. And a couple of men there with flashlights hollered "Hey, Rudy, over here." So I stopped and with their flashlights and with the help of other men we backed up to this home and got that body. By the time, we got home, there was another call. But nobody knew what was going on until the next morning. My wife, she said, "Well gee, what is it?" We already by that time had nine bodies.

When we went to pick up the second body over to Wilco Hill, coming back in my hearse I told this boy, "Joe, I'm getting sick." So I had to vomit, right on the street! It just come on me so fast. But after I let it out, I was all right, and my wife just keep feeding me orange juice. That's all I was eating or drinking, nothing else; that's all.

The importance of ensuring minimal civic services and avoiding public panic during a critical pollution situation would seem to require specific plans, yet Los Angeles has little more than the verbal proviso to shut down traffic.

Presumably the opportunity to forecast a severe situation might help in alerting the populace. Forecasting pollution, however, can prove just as embarrassing as forecasting weather. During a summer spell of clear skies, the Los Angeles Air Pollution Control District decided to release an optimistic report on advances in pollution control. One thankful headline writer wrote, "1970s Expected to Bring Victory in War on Smog." The day this headline appeared, the clear skies vanished and a three-day siege of smog set in. One enraged person called a district official and declared in a deadly serious voice, "You guys have a smog faucet that you can turn on and off when you want to tap the public till," to which the district's public information officer replied, "Boy, did we goof on that one."

By the time air pollution officials in New York decided to call one severe air pollution alert, the severe levels had passed. The lack of a timely warning could have proved more than just embarrassing. Fortunately, the episode occurred over a Thanksgiving weekend, and the decline in commuter traffic emissions and industrial emissions reduced hazards. At the same time, a mild weather spell reduced heating demands and emissions. Pollution protection efforts can still lie largely in the hands of fate instead of man.

In the face of such specters, pollution adaption proponents can do a complete reversal of form. The emphasis on adaption can be replaced by a stress on the imminent success of control efforts. "The main battle against smog has been won," Chrysler official Charles Heinen announced in 1969. Shortly thereafter, Dr. Fred Bowditch of General Motors announced, "The peak output of automobile-producing smog on Southern California definitely has passed—and will never be as high again." As in the case of the optimistic announcement by Los Angeles air pollution officials, such optimism by waste generators can collide with reality. The Bowditch announcement, for instance, just managed to precede Los Angeles's three-day seige of smog. This misguided optimism stems in part from a rather simplistic approach to waste control. The auto officials had based their victory claims on exhaust controls over one set of emissions—hydrocarbons —and ignored the increase in oxides of nitrogen and the ever-rising number of autos on the road.

Such oversights can generate a more modest approach. The chairman of the American Petroleum Institute's Committee on Air and Water Pollution recently addressed a Los Angeles audience. According to a Los Angeles *Times* report, "He [Kerryn King] said Los Angeles had been founded 188 years ago, that it had taken all that time for the current pollution problems to develop and that realisticly citizens could not expect solutions overnight." King then noted, "You will ultimately have a pollution-free internal combustion engine." King then gave a hint of how soon "ultimately" might be. "We can go along for another 10 to 15 years as we are now."

The patient approach, although calmly rational, can suffer from serious defects. The waste victim's tolerance for the status quo rarely matches the tolerance a waste generator can afford. "Overnight" for Los Angeles citizens has already meant 26 years of living with smog and 16 years of trying to get controls on the internal combustion engine. To Los Angeles, 10 more years of patience means that much more exposure to the known and unknown risks of smog. The Los Angeles *Times* editorialized, "Unfortunately southern California may not survive that long a wait for clean air. And certainly its citizens do not intend to put up with any such delay."

the environmental movement

Intolerance for pollution adaption generates a relatively new political constituency, the environmentalists. This constituency reflects the broad range of pollution victims: urban residents, sportsmen, school-age parents, college students, recreationists, conservationists, tourist interests—as well as scientists and engineers concerned with the traditional "deafening silence of the universities." Organization-wise, this constituency can range from conservation groups such as Audubon and Sierra Club to urban groups like Stamp Out Smog (SOS) in Los Angeles and Get Oil Out (GOO) in Santa Barbara. These groups can accommodate an amazing range of political bedfellows, from conservative property owners to militant students. The environmentalists find common ground in the goal of protecting the natural and human environment from pollution and degradation. To environmentalists, uncertainty over pollution effects is not reason for caution but action. "With so many possible long-term or chronic effects involved, the lesson of preventive medicine would be to eliminate or reduce pollution without regard to the establishment of specific cause and effect," observes Michigan State University botanist John Cantlon. Dr. Eric Cassell is a New York physician deeply concerned with air pollution: "Now is not the time to worry whether we have proved whether any specific pollutant causes any specific disease. We have produced sufficient evidence that pollution of the environment is bad for health, and that this warrants prevention or control of any pollution of the total environment.'' Such a perspective tends to leapfrog the traditional fragmentation of waste control and specialization of knowledge.

"Let us accept that clean environment is a healthy environment and that the total concept is worth fighting and struggling for, even though our science is also currently inadequate," says Dr. Cassell. Preoccupation with material progress and economic growth becomes secondary to environmental considerations. "Since we have the capability of providing a comfortable environment, why live with less just because someone says it won't hurt us?" public health consultant Ron Linton asks rhetorically.

Being citizen-based rather than professional in nature, environmental groups generally must depend on volunteer expertize, donations, and labor. The environmentalists have often been effective in educating and informing the public to pollution threats to the environment and to humans. They find a responsive audience in a society with a high standard of living and a cheapened environment in which to enjoy it. A series of popular books on the environmental predicament for example, *Moment in the Sun, The Population Bomb,* the Sierra Club Wilderness editions, *Silent Spring*—have spearheaded this campaign of environmental concern at the same time Southern California Edison and the National Coal Association have been propounding the virtues of pollution adaption and patience. The same material progress that provides people with postindustrial leisure also provides the time and the need to become involved with environmental issues.

Generally the environmental groups have been oriented to particular problems—an airport intruding on the Florida Everglades, a dam intruding on the Grand Canyon, or a power plant smokestack intruding on the urban scene. Although the environmental groups have achieved notable successes—including blockage of a major metropolitan jetport on the Florida Everglades, these successes are often limited and only of lingering duration. Often, citizen groups become aware of the pollution risks of a particular new activity or development once it is well underway with considerable political and economic momentum, as in the case of DDT. The ensuing conservationist-polluter "battles" make sprightly news stories as charges and countercharges of "blocking progress" and "destroying the planet" are exchanged. The environmentalists are often at a distinct disadvantage in these battles because they lack access to critical information and the expertise to analyze the information that private and public agencies enjoy. In this information gap, the environmentalists, deeply committed to ideals of environmental quality, are prone to transform potential pollution risks into unproved dangers. In a noise abatement study, a Council of Europe report found that some noise control groups tended to overdramatize the health dangers of noise to muster public support. This "propaganda against noise," according to the report, alienated public support while the people "who are most aroused are the rationalizing neurotics and paranoiacs and, under certain circumstances, this may cause a wave of protracted lawsuits prompted by litigious paranoiacs." A waste generator can turn this misinformed dedication to his own purposes by disproving the allegations of an environmental group rather than by proving the safety of his waste control measures.

The supposed "referee" in these battles, a government regulatory agency, may share the resource preoccupations of the parties it is supposed to be regulating. In leasing the Santa Barbara Channel to Union Oil Company and other offshore drillers, the Department of the Interior tended to regard Santa Barbara citizens who raised questions of pollution and environmental safeguards as pests to be suffered or scorned. "I cannot see how these people can expect us to absorb any additional revenue losses merely because of their further obsession to protect their view," was the evaluation one Interior official, Cordell Moore, placed on this concern in an interdepartmental communication resurrected during Congressional hearings on the Union Oil blowout. In trying to discourage public hearings on the feasibility of offshore leases, another official, Eugene Stanley, observed, "We had tried to warn L.A. District Corps of Engineers of what he faced and we preferred not to stir the natives up any more than possible."

One Santa Barbara resident, supporting proposals for a marine sanctuary in the channel, testified before Congress, "Oil rights must not be permitted to obliterate the rights of Americans to enjoy uncluttered ocean views, unpolluted seascapes and beaches, and unimpaired fisheries. A series of residential communities that have been conscientious about zoning on shore are shocked to find themselves powerless to insist on zoning and other orderly, balanced development principles offshore." An Interior official, successfully opposing the sanctuary proposal, testified, "The willingness of the oil and gas industry to bid $603 million for drilling and production rights indicates the potentially large oil deposits that underlie the channel area . . . Every effort has been made to place specifications on these operations so that they will be conducted with a minimum of impact on other values in the channel." Seven months later, the communities along the Santa Barbara Channel were treated to the Union Oil blowout that more than justified the concern of the resident, Fred Eissler, then a Sierra Club director. Ironically, the Interior official held the post of Assistant Secretary for Fish, Wildlife, and Parks. The residents with the gummed-up shoreline and the fishermen with the oil-coated nets began to feel a personal kinship with the Indians whose buffalo plains and river valleys were recruited for empire by our forefathers.

As in the case of the Santa Barbara oil leases, the environmentalists have too often responded to, rather than initiated, actions designed to control and prevent waste pollution. They have literally been fighting on battlefields carefully chosen, studied, and laid out by their adversaries. Thus, while the environmental movement is broadly based, articulate, dedicated, and growing, it has so far lacked the professional and political means to effectively integrate goals of environmental protection into private and public decision-making. It has shown an ability to frustrate some exercises in pollution adaption. Despite its extensive ad campaign with the man holding the flashlight, Southern California Edison found its plans for coastal power plant expansion blocked by an aroused public. This sort of standoff between material progress and environmental quality, however, is hardly a solution. Because of the inherent futility of these stand-offs, waste generators as well as waste victims are now considering other alternatives, including the possibility of adapting existing institutions to the needs of waste control instead of the opposite. This approach focuses attention on two waste strategies traditional control methods have tended to ignore.

SUGGESTED READINGS

POLLUTION ADAPTION AND ACCEPTANCE

Curtis and Hogan, *op. cit.,* chap. 17 ("Where There's a Stack"). *See also* Atomic Energy Commission, *Nuclear Reactors* and *The New Force of Atomic Energy;* Hal Stroube, "Public Acceptance of Nuclear Power," *Nuclear Power Reactor Siting,* Atomic Energy Commission Conference; Dr. Glenn Seaborg, address to National Academy of Science at Argonne Laboratory, available from Atomic Energy Commission.

Dreisbach, Robert, *Handbook of the San Francisco Region,* Palo Alto, Calif.: Environmental Studies, 1969. A 576-page report by a Stanford University toxicologist on how waste pollution threatens to destroy one region.

Federal Aviation Agency, *Aircraft Noise and Community Relations,* published and distributed by the FAA's Western Regional Office in Los Angeles, undated. *See also* FAA, *Sounds of the Twentieth Century,* Washington, D.C.: U.S. Government Printing Office, 1961. J. H. Wiggins, "Sonic Boom Testing," paper delivered at 15th annual Institute of Environmental Sciences conference, Anaheim, Calif., *FAA Paper,* April 23, 1969. *See also* William Close (Department of Transportation), "Transportation Noise Environments of the Traveler and the Spectator," paper delivered at 15th annual Institute of Environmental Sciences conference, Anaheim, Calif., *FAA Papers,* April 23, 1969. Reflects how

pollution: adaption or control?

industry responds to noise reduction when it becomes a competitive advantage.

Los Angeles Air Pollution Control District, "The Alert System," *See also* " ℞ for Heavy Smog Attacks," paper prepared for the district by the Los Angeles County Medical Association. For air filtration systems, see "How Activated Charcoal 'Traps' Odors," *Air Engineering,* March, 1959; and Hurley Motley et al., "Effect of Polluted Los Angeles Air (Smog) on Lung Volume Measurements," *Journal of the American Medical Association,* November 14, 1959. Literature on air filtration available from Barnebey-Cheney Co., Columbus, Ohio. In the hearings by the Senate Subcommittee on Air and Water Pollution, (*Air Pollution–1968,* pt. I, pp. 137–158), Harvey Lieber, a Rutgers University political scientist, examines the shortcomings of New York regional air management and is rebutted by regional air official Alexander Rihm. See Los Angeles *Times* editorials of August 24 and September 4, 1969, for critique of pollution patience. Al Wiman, "A Breath of Death," Los Angeles: Flamingo Press, 1967, available on request from Los Angeles radio station KLAC and is a reprint of the excellent broadcast interview series.

Senate Subcommittee on Air and Water Pollution, *Water Pollution–1969.* pt. IV, pp. 1305 ff. Testimony and material on question of insurance liability for environmental disasters. *See also* Curtis and Hogan, *op. cit.,* chap. 15 (on radiation liability).

ENVIRONMENTAL MOVEMENT

Carson, Rachel, *op. cit.*

Dasmann, Raymond, *The Destruction of California,* New York: Macmillan, 1965; also available in paperback.

De Bell, Garrett, ed., *The Environmental Handbook,* New York: Ballantine, 1970. Selection of environmental readings for First National Environmental Teach-In, April 22, 1970.

Godfrey, Arthur, "Man and His Environment: A View Toward Survival," address before 13th National Conference of U.S. National Commission for UNESCO at San Francisco, November 24, 1969.

Margolis, Jon, "Our Country 'Tis of Thee, Land of Ecology," *Esquire* Magazine, March, 1970. An interesting and incisive review of the growth of the environmental movement. At end, however, the writer slights the willingness of environmentalists to forgo material comforts on behalf of environmental protection, an impression that could have been corrected had the writer been present for entire duration of the environmental conference.

Rienow, R., and L. Rienow, *Moment in the Sun,* New York: Dial Press, 1967; Ballantine paperback, 1969.

Senate Subcommittee on Air and Water Pollution, *Water Pollution—1969,* pts. 2–4. Extensive testimony on the letting of the Santa Barbara oil leases and the aftermath. For the community relations of another federal waste generator, the Atomic Energy Commission, *see* Curtis and Hogan, *op. cit.* chap. 12 ("Absolute Power").

7
plagiarizing nature

During one recent summer in New York City, restaurants could serve a glass of water only on customer request because of a severe water shortage. Yet three times the amount of water consumed daily by the city was flowing down the Hudson River and into the ocean—unusable because of pollution. Across the continent, the creeks in semi-arid Santee, California, lay parched under the summer sun. Yet fishermen, swimmers, boaters, and picnickers were enjoying a chain of five artificial lakes; the water in this aquatic playground came from the community's domestic sewage.

The summer contrast between Santee and New York City illustrates the benefits of processing wastes for use rather than transfer. Waste recycling reflects nature's concept of treating products of decay and waste for the enhancement of the environment.

Plagiarizing nature's style of waste control is not new. Farmers and ranchers have traditionally fertilized their fields with manure abundantly distributed by grazing livestock. Chinese farmers traditionally collect their defecation ("night soil") to regenerate their fields. Many enterprising young men earned their way through college by collecting restaurant garbage for farmers who used it as swill to raise corpulent pigs. Japan muscled its way to industrial and military prowess through its skill in transforming scrap iron, waste paper, and string into profitable products and guns. After Japan entered World War II, she was economically strapped because she could no longer be the world's trash scavenger. Such waste reuse was based less on an appreciation for ecology and aesthetics than on the attractive economics involved. As the economic appeal recedes, so does waste reuse. Sanitary regulations that require that swill be precooked puts restaurant garbage into Dempster Dumpsters rather than into the mouths of pigs. The cost of separating, processing, and marketing urban wasteloads has generally been regarded as far more expensive than simply transferring them elsewhere. Modern affluence, with its stress on rapid obsolescence and consumer convenience, can work at cross-purposes with reuse. Industrial economist Arsen Darnay observed in an issue of *Environmental Science and Technology:*

Each deposit-type bottle displaced from the market means the sale of 20 one-way containers, since deposit bottles make an average of 20 trips to the home before they are broken. In 1966, for instance, 65 billion containers were filled, but only 28 billion containers were produced. If all containers were of returnable type, a market for 37 billion units would have been up for the taking, and that's a lot of bottles and cans.

The zenith of rapid obsolescence has been jokingly described as the Cadillac owner who trades in his car when the ashtrays are full. The costly shortcomings of conventional waste control, however, can make waste recovery increasingly feasible and competitive. At the same time, the increasing cost and scarcity of virgin materials encourages interest in the potential of secondary or recovered materials.

wastewater reclamation

In 1959, the San Diego suburb of Santee suffered the inevitable pains of fast-tract growth: an increasing demand for water and an increasing load of toilet effluent. The conventional remedy in southern California is to transfer the waste waterload to the nearest ocean outfall system and increase fresh water imports from northern California and the Colorado River via 100-mile-long dam and aqueduct systems. Santee officials wondered if a water-short problem and a water-surplus problem might not complement each other sufficiently to form a solution through wastewater reclamation.

Although river water may be used six or seven times by downstream communities, water reclamation refers to the use of treated sewage or effluent direct from the treatment facility. Secondary sewage treatment leaves less than .1 percent of impurities, and advanced (or tertiary) treatment can render effluent suitable for a wide variety of uses. As usual, economics and public reaction have been traditional constraints. Advanced treatment can cost twice that of secondary treatment, and this investment can be countered by public sensitivities. In 1957 a prolonged drought encouraged Chanute, Kansas, to process and recycle its effluent into the drinking supply. The treated effluent met health standards, but its pale yellow color, musty taste and frothy appearance at the tap encouraged a run on bottled water until the drought ended.

With this history, water reclamation has often been limited to cooling of industrial processes and irrigation of cotton, cut flowers, golf course grass, and other nonedible crops; reclaimed water irrigates Golden Gate Park and helps keep the Floating Gardens of Mexico bouyant.

The Santee County Water District overcame such obstacles by carefully integrating the water reclamation efforts into the broad economic and social needs of the community (see Figures 13 and 14). The district found one customer for reclaimed water: a land developer with the responsibility of keeping a 160-acre golf course irrigated with increasingly expensive imported water. The rising price of imported water also made aquatic recreation economically unfeasible in a semi-arid community; reclaimed water held forth this opportunity. A creek basin scarred by gravel extraction and used as an impromptu dump provided a possible site for artificial lakes. The gravelly bed also provided a natural means of filtration for treated water. The willingness of a modest

*man
and his
environment:
waste*

figure 13. *Creekbed scarred by gravel excavation will be restored as recreation lake through Santee Water Reclamation program. Note tree mound in center that will serve as an island.*

community to embark on such an ambitious program of water reuse attracted the support and the necessary recources of five government agencies: the Federal Water Quality Control Administration, the California State Department of Public Health, the California State Department of Water Resources, the California State Department of Fish and Game, and the San Diego County Health Department.

Today Santee domestic sewage goes into a water reclamation plant, through the gravel bed, through a chlorination unit, through the chain of five artificial lakes and onto the golf course. The lakes average about 1000 feet in length and are up to 10 feet deep. In 1966 more than 125,000 people swam or fished in their effluent, their confidence gained by full disclosure of a careful monitoring program of water quality. (The public eagerness for aquatic recreation was such that Ray Stoyer, the water district manager, one morning found 50 persons swimming in water that had not yet been tested and opened to the public.)

In a recreational lake setting, water reuse tends to sell itself, particularly if civic neighbors are sweltering in summer heat. (Residents take pride in bringing guests to

figure 14. *Gravel excavation in creekbed after restoration as recreation lake in Santee water reclamation program.*

the lakes.) In the Santee lakes channel catfish, bass, and trout were planted; fish production averages over 400 pounds per acre per year, although at times there has been an adverse ratio of pan to game fish. Small sailboats and row boats ply between picnic islands; a rope-connected ferry also reaches the islands. Gravel excavation operations carefully cut around the islands to leave native vegetation, including handsome sycamore trees, intact. Artists enjoy a blue lake and green shore set off by a dun-colored landscape. This contrast also helps land developers attract residential clients. Wastewater reuse has thus given a semi-arid community the opportunity to swim, fish, and boat and at the same time to relieve the wasteload pressures on the offshore.

The problems as well as the successes of the Santee lakes are instructive. A surge in coliform counts raised fears of inadequate sanitary treatment. However, the surge was traced to an influx of migratory waterfowl; the lakes are now a bird-watching attraction. The reclamation process cannot completely reduce the nutrient-rich traits of wastewater; nutrient-fueled algae blooms have triggered fish kills involving up to 40,000 fish. Aquatic plants that assimilate the nutrients have been utilized to help ward off sludge banks and eutrophication. Swimmers tended to stir up disturbing turbidity in the lakes. Reclaimed water was shunted into an adjacent swimming pool to provide swimming. However, because of the present expense of removing potassium permanganate that can color the water brown and create aesthetic problems, Santee reverted to imported water for its swimming pool after four seasons of using reclaimed water. Santee officials feel they have effectively demonstrated the technical feasibility of using reclaimed water for swimming and meeting health requirements. Potassium permanganate is a disinfectant and deodorizing agent introduced in the chlorination process. Manganese and iron may also be picked up in the natural filtration step of reclamation, according to the FWQCA, and create color and removal problems.

Over-all, Santee officials and the cooperating government agencies have found the reclamation project a sound economic as well as social investment. Reclaimed water run through the natural filtration beds costs between $8 and $10 per acre-foot. A $1.7-million advanced water treatment plant will provide artificial filtration and expand the water reclamation capacity. The water cost with this new plant will jump to $30 to $40 per acre-foot. However, imported water in 1968 cost the district $42 per acre-foot and is expected to jump to $75 in the next decade. Moreover, the demineralization process in the treatment plant will produce water of better quality than the imported river water. Salinity in the Colorado River is on the increase because of upriver utilization, and the water reclamation plant will actually reduce the dissolved solids content of the imported water. The high-quality performance of the treatment plant will allow the reclaimed water to be introduced into the community's drinking water supply. A community wastewater distribution system will irrigate a college campus, another golf course, and supply more lakes. An upstream dam system to meet metropolitan San Diego water needs disrupted Santee's former agricultural economy and dried up the creek bed in which the lakes now lie. Reclaimed water will now permit this economy to be revived where appropriate as well as provide a possible inducement to industries with water needs.

Water reuse is beginning to assert its potential in a variety of projects. Under contract from the state of Pennsylvania, Westinghouse is building a treatment facility to trap and reclaim five million gallons of acid mine drainage annually that now poisons the Susquehanna River. The reclaimed water will be sold to industry at competitive prices to avoid billing the taxpayers in the long run. Over the years farmers and citrus ranchers in Orange County, California, have overdrafted underground water recources. Salt-water intrusion from the neighboring Pacific Ocean seeps into the depleted reservoirs and jeopardizes remaining underground water resources. A pilot water reclamation plant next to the Orange County Sanitation District has pumped reclaimed water into the underground reservoirs to resist the ocean and replenish fresh water supplies. Plans now call for diluting the reclaimed water with another water source to reduce high mineral counts. Percolation—the spreading of treated effluent over the ground for filtration and absorption into underground reservoirs—is another method of man-aided water recycling.

Smudge pots in fruit orchards often contribute more to air pollution then to frost control. When frost descended on one Oregon fruit orchard, an overhead sprinkling system bathed trees in warm water. Frost damage was resisted. The warm water came from the cooling system of a nearby paper mill. This experimental project supported by the Federal Water Quality Control Administration may transform the threat of thermal pollution into a major agricultural safeguard where conditions are favorable. The thermal generator can reduce his treatment costs while the farmer can expand his productivity and, possibly, even his growing season. The value of warm water as a soil conditioner is also being studied.

With water costs, wastewater treatment costs, and wastewater standards all rising, industry finds in-plant water reuse increasingly attractive. It permits a partial return on treatment investment. Many industrial water needs, such as cooling, do not require a very high degree of treatment. In 1941 after a study by water engineer Abel Wolman, the Bethlehem Steel Company at Sparrows Point, Maryland, began to buy 100 million gallons of treated effluent from Baltimore daily for cooling and process water. This effluent required less preliminary treatment than nearby waterway sources plagued by high chloride counts. Bethlehem's success has helped inspire other applications of industrial water reuse. Instead of the typical 40,000 to 65,000 gallons of water per ton of steel produced, the Fontana Division of Kaiser Steel Company uses only 1,400 gallons, equivalent to a recirculation of 2,800 to 4,600 per cent, or reuse of water about 35 times. Fontana is in southern California, where water economy has its particular financial rewards.

Such reuse has social significance beyond mere water quality. Edward Ackerman and George Löf note, in *Technology in America Water Development,* "Increased water reuse also will make possible the establishment of more industry in water-scarce areas. Extreme water conservation measures can free even such large water users as steel and paper mills from requirements for location on seacoasts and large rivers."

Exploitation of the nutrient values of effluent is under study. Instead of increased treatment costs to remove these nutrients, Dr. Harold Gotaas of Northwestern University suggests that nutrient-triggered algae blooms be harvested for food value, particularly in euthrophication-prone lakes. Methods of harvesting and processing present great and unsolved obstacles. Carefully controlled effluent could become the means of fertilizing estuarine areas and realizing the promise of aquaculture. Heated wastewater is used quite liberally in Russian fish culture, and heated effluent from a nuclear power plant has been utilitized with commercial success in the Long Island, New York, oyster industry.

The power generation potential of water reuse is also being seriously considered. Storm overloads from Chicago's combined system of sewer and storm drains can counter the city's expensive investment in improved sewage treatment. Separating the system could be very costly and needless. The Chicago Sanitary District now has plans to excavate huge caverns beneath the city, well below the groundwater level. Peak wasteloads during storms would be stored in these caverns for later treatment. At this point, the electric power industry, short of water to generate power, enters the picture. The stored water, run through reversible pump turbines, would serve to generate power. Such water storage also appeals to Chicago's neighbors. By being able to hold storm water for treatment, Chicago would not pass pollution downstream. The treated storm water could also be diverted to the lake if need be. Chicago's traditional means of protecting its cherished lakefront from water pollution has been diversion of runoff downstate. This tactic, although successful, has raised the possibility of lower lake levels and endangered navigation.

Overflows from a combined storm and sewer drain system in the District of Columbia pollute the Anacostia River. The Federal Water Quality Control Administration now plans to store these overflows in a wasteland dump. Part of the dumping grounds will be reclaimed as a water treatment pond; the remainder will be divided into two recreational lakes supplied by the pond. These recreational lakes will offer one activity foreign to the Santee lakes: ice skating. The recreational potential of this land-mending project has attracted the National Park Service as one of the planners.

If the potential for water reuse is attractive, so is the opportunity. Some 60 to 90 percent of the water delivered to a city may leave via waste discharges. With technology such a latecomer to the field of waste reuse, more economical systems under development may reduce the high cost significantly. (Activated charcoal's filtering ability can trap hard-to-treat synthetic detergents; but mineral salts still continue to defy activiated charcoal as well as other filtering devices.) Ray Stoyer, the Santee Water official who is now Director of Planning for the Irvine Ranch Water District in southern California, is testing the pressure pipe wastewater treatment. Under the PPT system, primary sewage effluent is introduced into pressurized lines that serve to treat, transport, and distribute the treated effluent to specific water users. This concept eliminates the need for large secondary sewage treatment plants and provides a distribution system for reclaimed water. Oxygen and activated sludge from an aerobic digester are injected into the pressure pipelines to effect treatment.

Bacteria in the sludge serve to assimilate organic wastes. Because most sewage collecting systems utilize gravity feed to effect collection, the pressurized pipes serve to pump the collected effluent back uphill to effect distribution.

Without such prospective advances, water reclamation is already cheaper than the much-publicized desalinization of sea water. With its dissolved salts, sea water contains more than 35 times as much foreign matter as secondary sewage effluent.

With its economic utility regained, reclaimed water can help pay for its treatment, something that secondary treatment effluent can never do. This factor, coupled with the rising cost and decreasing quality of imported water, promises to make wastewater reclamation an increasingly attractive alternative to wastewater transfer.

In the enthusiasm for water reclamation, some sewage treatment agencies are renaming their treatment facilities "water reclamation" without acquiring the proper capability. One renamed municipal agency in southern California put its effluent into an underground aquifer. However, the quality of the effluent was such that it could not be withdrawn for use. When the aquifer filled, the agency diverted the low-quality effluent into a creekbed that emptied into the Pacific Ocean. This diversion brought strong criticism from the San Diego Regional Water Quality Board, and the local agency is now under pressure to live up to its name.

Another negative aspect to enthusiasm for water reclamation is that Santee officials have been less than candid with visitors in disclosing the switchover from reclaimed water to imported water in the swimming pool. After the switchover, this pool sign still remained: "This swimming facility has opened a few field of recreational opportunity for the American public. It is supplied with reclaimed water." The environmental field need be no more immune than the resource field from promotional indulgence.

The promise of water reclamation may also be impaired if increasing sewage dumping of nondegradable substances, particularly mineral salts, cancels out treatment improvement. "Concentrative pollution" can result when counts of mineral salts rise as water is used and reused. Industrial waste lines that bypass strong effluent to special treatment facilities can be one means of reducing such pressures.

wastes to shape the landscape by
The reuse potential in solid wastes can be as diverse and as inviting as that of wastewater. A hill is now growing above the flat terrain of Virginia Beach, Virginia. The aborning hill is being carefully landscaped and, when 60 feet high, will serve as a community amphitheatre and coasting ramp for soap box derbys. The hill is being built out of Virginia Beach's refuse. It will consume the refuse generated over a three-year period by a city of 150,000. A borrow pit that supplies soil cover for the hill will become a lake.

The Virginia Beach project illustrates the land-building and land-restoring potential of our solid wastes. Another flatland area, Chicago, is now preparing to generate a "mountain" out of refuse for summer hiking and winter skiing. The mountain would be 16 times higher than Virginia Beach's hill. When you have more trash generators, you can afford to build taller "Mt. Trashmores." Spoil from Chicago's excavated caverns for water storage could contribute to an artificial mountain range.

Such land-building potential cannot be realized merely by throwing trash down a gravel pit or gully. Indeed, sanitary fill, like all forms of waste reuse, carefully integrates the wastes into the environment. Groundwater contamination, decomposing fumes, and uneven settling must be averted by careful site selection and intermittent soil cover. This need for soil can sometimes restrict application of landfill in areas of rocky terrain, such as portions of West Virginia. (With many of its hills ravaged by strip mining, West Virginia could benefit by sanitary fill operations if an adequate soil supply is available.)

Land reclamation and land-building projects should focus on true wastelands, such as eroded gullies, old dumps, or hills scarred by strip mining, rather than on fertile marsh lands or other natural areas which may be within the more convenient reach of trash runs.

Allegany County, Maryland, is phasing out 87 roadside and open burning dumps, including one community dump conveniently located on a college campus, by diverting refuse to an abandoned strip mine scarred by 50-foot gouges. Western Maryland is amply supplied with over 2000 such landscape blights. These ugly depressions can swallow up prodigious wasteloads, with the exception of fly ash (too prone to blow away) and autos (too tough to compact). At first the advent of one mammoth dump aroused community fears over development of one mammoth rat haven ringed by wind-blown blizzards of debris. However, as noted by Wilfred Shields, chief of Maryland's Division of Solid Wastes:

These scars can be filled with earth and refuse so that the filled-in strip mine blends in with the contours of the surrounding landscape with no apparent evidence that the area had previously been raped of its resources and left as an eyesore for future generations.

Spoil piles from trenching operations provide ample soil cover. Diversion ditches and careful sloping and compaction prevent penetration of runoff into coal seams and the production of acid mine drainage. "If no water gets into the coal seam, none gets out," says Shields. In an interesting twist on wastewater treatment, planners on this particular project are planning to divert acid mine drainage into a *completed* landfill "to determine if the quality of the water is improved by running it through the buried refuse." (Through another form of waste management—materials reclamation, capital costs are reduced by retrieving discarded chairs as office furniture.) Such landscape redemption impresses private developers as well as hard-pressed refuse collectors. One Maryland developer is now eagerly promoting conversion of one strip mine into a ski resort.

By restoring wastelands, sanitary fill operations add value to the landscape. The restored wastelands can accommodate parks, golf courses, scenic areas and outdoor stages. Generally, landfill sites are restricted to relatively light development to avert the risk of settling. A public sanitary agency will often lease a piece of cull land for landfill only to see the private owner reap the rewards of land reclamation by opening up a private golf course or trailer park. Wiser public agencies are now purchasing the cull land themselves to reap the rewards of reclamation in the form of public recreation. Even one traditionally sacrosanct disposal site need not be immune from the potential for reuse. In Livermore, California, public officials converted an old foothill cemetery into a scenic park called Pioneer Memorial Park.

Frank Bowerman, a waste researcher with Aerojet-General Corporation, has suggested using New York subways in off-peak hours to haul wastes in specialized trains to harbor barges. The barges would then deposit the refuse offshore to generate artificial archipelagos suitable for recreation and even supersonic airports. Such schemes, highly appealing to overloaded refuse agencies and airport authorities bombarded by jet noise lawsuits, will have to be carefully balanced with nearshore ecology. With so many of the nation's largest cities on or near the oceanfront, the ocean looms as a prospective lifesaver for trash problems. While a five-year study by Harvard's School of Public Health and the University of Rhode Island's Graduate School of Oceanography finds some sea disposal feasible, the study's enthusiasm is limited to *incinerated* wastes dumped in water at least 100 feet deep to avoid drift and entanglement with fish nets. Acute and chronic toxicity tests in marine life showed no detectable damage from residual incinerated particles except those that lodged in fish gills or buried bottom creatures. The California Fish and Game Department has dumped auto wrecks off the coast to form flourishing artificial fish reefs. However, this form of dumping does not appear to be the salvation of crowded junkyard operators. Autos tend to rust away, and artificial reef builders now prefer more permanent quarry rock.

The subway-submarine disposal scheme suggests two of the limitations of sanitary fill: shortage of conveniently located sites and efficient transportation. As a city runs out of appropriate wasteland sites, the refuse runs become longer and more expensive. The refuse runs can add to urban traffic congestion and air pollution as a city must support refuse fleets of more than 100 trucks. Residential streets impressed into service as dump routes can become pedestrian hazards. Long-distance refuse hauls by railroad are now being seriously considered.

Many rural areas have a shortage of sanitary fill material and a surplus of eroded mining and farming land. The diversion of long-distance refuse hauls to such areas could become a means of regenerating derelict lands as well as local treasuries. Through waste ash applications, Great Britain has reclaimed over 2000 acres of derelict mining land for agriculture. In time, pipeline technology may be adapted to slurry transport of ground-up waste and thus obviate the need for truck or train refuse runs.

Besides its land-reclamation potential, refuse and garbage can condition and enrich the soil. Compost—the decomposed remains of garbage and refuse—can improve the workability of soil, its structure, its resistance to compaction and erosion, and its moisture regime. Germany's famed Riesling wines grow on the steep hillsides of the Rhine River. Generous applications of refuse compost enable these nearly vertical vineyards to resist slope erosion. In Holland one compost company processes the municipal wastes of eight cities and towns (one million inhabitants) into some 200,000 tons of compost annually (see Table 4).

Compost use in the United States has been very limited. Although rich in organic material, compost is weak in nutrients and farmers have found chemical fertilizers more economical to buy, transport, and apply. The rise of livestock feedlots generates another glut on the soil-conditioning market: steer manure. Even in Europe compost is utilized largely for luxury agriculture such as flowers and grapes. Processing costs of compost, including separation of iron, glass, and other inorganic refuse items, further reduces the competitive capability of compost. In Europe, where composting is most popular, composting operators utilize only 11 percent of Holland's refuse and only 1 percent of Germany's refuse load. Composting is generally suitable for only domestic refuse and not for industrial and commercial refuse, particularly demolition

table 4

sales distribution of compost from municipal refuse in Holland

outlet	1961	1965
Forestland improvement	2.4	0.6
Basic agriculture (field and row crops, and for pig litter)	34.4	16.4
Fruit farming	6.5	6.3
Hotbed vegetable farming [a]	11.6	13.0
Greenhouse vegetable farming	7.9	8.4
Flower and flower bulb production (greenhouse and outdoor)	11.7	17.6
City park, sportsfield, and recreational use	25.5	37.7

[a] Hotbed compost is freshly ground domestic refuse. It is used on the bottom of the hotbed in place of horse manure. The biological process of composting generates heat that makes the hotbed crop grow. Hotbed crops in Holland are cucumbers, melons, and green peppers.

Source: S. A. Hart, *Solid Waste Management—Composting; European Activity and American Potential,* Public Health Service pub. no. 1826, 1968.

debris. The bacterial action that breaks down organic matter works reluctantly on cellulose matter—scrap lumber, rubber products, pressed boards—and not at all on plastics and synthetics. Rags, papers, or filters soaked in solvents can destroy bacteria. These "compost reject" items are on the rise in solid wasteloads.

The growing costs of tussling with solid wasteloads is beginning to make forms of composting look more economical. In a report for the U.S. Public Health Service, *Composting: European Activity and American Potential,* agricultural engineer Samuel Hart suggests how the land might be used as a refuse burial site. Rough-quality compost would be spread over a land site; soil microbiological activity would degrade and stabilize remaining waste. "This concept of compost utilization might be likened to a biological incinerator," notes Hart. "Put bluntly, it would be insulting Mother Earth without quite violating her." Although concurrent land uses would probably be precluded, the land would not be lost to future use. Going a step further, the Public Health Service and the Tennessee Valley Authority are jointly studying reclamation of blighted mine sites with compost supplying organic conditioning. Mine tailings, like most mineral wastes, contain no nutrients, have poor soil texture, and many fine grains. Compost contains no large amounts of nutrients either, but the addition of partially treated sewage effluent—with its nutrient load of nitrogen and phosphorous—can make up for this lack. Hydromulching, a slurry of compost and grass seed, can impart soil-holding qualities to denuded areas and reduce sediment and acid mine discharges. The United States has much land that could benefit from such kind attention. Silt loads from highway cut-and-fill operations could be controlled. Department of Agriculture figures show that two billion acres of land lay despoiled by surface mining, including the coal and iron fields of Pennsylvania and the phosphate fields of Florida. Instead of generating food crops, these lands generate the silt loads and acid mine drainage that effectively counteract municipal investment in water pollution control. Even for an affluent country, such tolerance for derelict lands can be expensive. Land reclamation projects offer the opportunity to reverse this costly desecration and reduce the solid wastes problem at the same time. As in the Santee water reclamation project, waste reuse becomes increasingly attractive when broad public, rather then strictly local, factors are considered. Because Pennsylvania now requires strip miners to restore, contour, or terrace a mine before abandonment, some 10,000 acres in bituminous regions are being farmed or used for recreation and building.

A city goes to considerable expense to filter, burn, and then dispose of digested sludge, the solid residues from treated sewage. The Federal Water Quality Control Administration and Chicago are now investing in a million-dollar project to use the fertilizing values of sludge to enrich sandy soils and raise field corn and pasture grasses. By the year 2015, some 21,500 acres of soil-poor land is expected to absorb Chicago's sludge load via pipe and spray irrigation techniques and raise agricultural income by $580,000 yearly. Dr. Louis Kardos at Pennsylvania State University has conducted successful experiments in irrigating and fertilizing field and forest crops with treated effluent (see "The Living Landscape Filter" *Landscape Architecture,* April, 1969). Under federal grants poultry offal and broiler litter are being studied as livestock feed. Degradation of waste paper into livestock protein through fermentation is being evaluated by chemist John Duros at the Denver Research Institute. Chemist Seymour Block of the University of Florida has demonstrated that municipal refuse, when properly fortified and composted, can help produce mushrooms in good yield and flavor.

Because composting provides a partial means of recovering waste treatment costs, some municipal refuse agencies are instituting new composting systems. Gainesville, Florida, where chemist Block nurtures his mushrooms on garbage, is building a compost plant for its municipal refuse with the help of a federal grant. Both refuse and sludge will be blended into compost. Incoming refuse goes on conveyor belts, and refuse pickers remove cardboard, metal, and rags, which are sold as salvage. Given the refuse rise in compost rejects, such separation is essential.

Compression, rather than composting, is serving to excite the imagination of other municipal refuse agencies. The Tezuka Refuse Compression System in Japan reduces refuse into blocks that, when dipped into asphalt or concrete, become "building blocks." A Japanese school is presently being built with such building blocks. What especially pleases a refuse operator is that such a waste-handling concept requires no separation of materials. Garbage and junk metal can be mixed and compressed. Binding of the blocks is enhanced by the starchy nature of the Japanese diet, especially rice.

Building blocks would be more useful to a city than compost, but the alluring compression concept still has to prove itself. Even when fully enclosed and sealed, compressed refuse bales could produce methane gas through anaerobic biodegradation and eventually rupture the bale enclosure. This type of possibility doesn't seem designed to revolutionize the building miterials industry. Compression and compaction techniques appear more realistic, if not so glamorous, when viewed as a means of expanding the longevity of sanitary landfill.

materials reclamation

The refuse pickers in Gainesville illustrate another resource potential in solid wastes: secondary materials use. The market for secondary materials has generated its own unique labor force of ragpickers, Boy Scout newspaper drives, and dump scavengers. A recent proposal to transform a dump in Rio de Janeiro into a sanitary landfill encountered vigorous opposition from Rio's vocal colony of dump scavengers. Because of the traditional reliance on cheap or charitable labor to undertake processing, secondary materials recovery has tended to decline in an affluent nation like the United States. Changes in production made without regard for reusability contributes to this decline. American steel processes have been refined—or overrefined—to the point that metal recovery is often ruled out by the presence of certain impurities. Special inks used in printing often complicate, if not eliminate, reprocessing of waste paper. A rag scavenger in New York complained to *The Wall Street Journal* that miniskirts were cutting down on his volume. Materials recovery so dependent on market economics and fashions can often become an ironic detriment to the goal of waste recycling. The advent of the internal combustion engine transformed a waste by-product of kerosene production into the world's most profitable product and the atmosphere's principal curse: gasoline.

As in water reclamation, increasing standards and investment in waste treatment fosters a new economic incentive for materials reclamation. Industry finds that recovery of acids, chemicals, and liquors from wastewater provides a partial means of recovering treatment costs. Instead of trucking spent pickle liquor to a dump, a Milwaukee steel plant now trucks this powerful rust remover to a municipal sewage plant to remove algae-promoting phosphorous from effluent discharges into Lake Michigan. Even waste air can produce some revenue. Fly ash collected from industrial smokestacks and air incinerators is used in filters and in building roads. Heat and methane gas generated by bacterial decomposition of sludge provides auxilliary heat and power for many sewage treatment plants.

Such modest recovery operations are being accomplished despite a glaring gap in technology. Industrial economist Arsen Darnay, Jr., notes:

We may ask ourselves why it is that we find uses for the bark of trees, process trash fish to make nutritious fish meal, are able to utilize every component of an animal carcass to produce valuable goods, and squeeze high-priced commodities from every fraction of crude oil; but are unwilling to prevent the squandering of valuable natural resources after they have been converted into finished goods. The answer seems to be that whereas we have perfected the technologies necessary to harvest, separate, refine, and convert virgin materials—no matter how complicated their chemical structure or how heterogeneous the mixtures in which we find them —we have not made any strides toward using secondary materials resources because we have had no need to do so.

In Denver a hammer mill reduces an automobile into a series of fist-sized pellets in 60 seconds. Some 500 junk cars can be "pellitized" daily. The hammer mill is cleaning up a two-year accumulation of junk cars stacked in piles around Denver. When this cleanup is finished in six months, the hammer mill will digest the junk auto backlog throughout Colorado. This hammer mill is operated by a private rather than a public agency, National Metal Processing Co. Through its $2-million investment in modern, semiautomated technology, the company makes materials recovery profitable. One ton of processed scrap pellets enables a steelmaker to eliminate the need to mine 1½ tons of iron ore, 1 ton of coke, and ½ ton of limestone.

Waste generators themselves are beginning to focus more sophisticated attention on secondary materials use. Tires pose a particularly irksome waste problem, fouling waste incinerators and subverting landfills. "You think you have buried a tire under dirt only to see it pop up again like air," one landfill operator said. Tire resue has traditionally been limited to backyard swings, tugboat bumpers, and, among the thrifty southeast Asians, shoes. Gale Sayers and other shifty halfbacks improve their running ability by hopping about spare tires. Although used tires retain up to 80 percent of their total manufacturing value, less than one-fourth of the tires removed from use are recapped, another reflection of America's affluent obsession with virgin products. (The rate of tire recapping in other countries runs as high as 80 percent.) Extensive research by Firestone Tire and Rubber Company and the U.S. Bureau of Mines now discloses that shredded tires could become a source of energy and chemicals. By exposing shedded tires to the same process used in coking coal, a ton of scrap rubber yielded 140 gallons of liquid oils, 1500 cubic feet of gas (equivalent in heat value to natural gas), and a solids residue of friable, high-carbon-content material. To tap scrap tires—which have a higher heat value then coal—for power generation, England is perfecting a clean-air tire incinerator.

The opportunity for materials reuse can be enhanced if products are designed with this end in mind. Observes the Committee on Resources and Man, National Academy of Sciences—National Research Council, in its report, *Resources and Man:*

The automobile is a prime target for improvement. The copper content of the average car should be reduced from about 1.4 percent to 0.4 percent or less of the total carcass and problems of recovery simplified. The metals involved could then be used repeatedly, with greatly reduced waste and with elimination of unsightly modes of disposal. New methods of combining metals in clad structures, for instance, makes it possible to utilize the desired properties of special metals such as copper with greater economy, better structural properties, and reduction to levels that eliminate the adverse effects of mixing.

The application of automatic sensor technology to refuse sorting could help make municipal refuse slavaging operations competitive again. This path is being pursued by a private refuse processor, Metropolitan Waste Conversion Corporation. Centrifugal force, ballistic separation, and magnetic separation can lend themselves to this concept. Effective refuse salvaging can make composting that much more feasible. Technology is also being developed to exploit the compost and salvage rejects. A high-temperature waste converter (1400 to 1500 degrees F) reduces cellulose, plastics, neoprenes, synthetics, solvents, and woods into usable elemental carbon and combustible gases. Part of the gases produced keep the converter running on a self-sustaining basis. This converter, developed by Pan American Resources of Pomona, California, meets air pollution standards and is being utilized by the city of Houston and by harried scavenger companies in the San Francisco Bay area.

Recently a full-page ad in the national magazines declared, "Our Scrap Heaps Can Be Aluminum Mines." This encouraging interest in waste reuse by an aluminum company stemmed less from a technological advance than another incentive for waste reuse. A number of bills in state legislatures would prohibit the use of throwaway aluminum cans. These proposed bills are designed to meet a lack noted by Stewart Udall when he was Secretary of the Interior. "I happen to think, just to be specific, that the aluminum beer can, for example, is a disaster. It doesn't degrade. It will be there a hundred years from now, shining in the sun, and yet there is nothing to prohibit its manufacture," observed Udall before a joint House-Senate Colloquium on environmental quality. Prospective waste prevention measures can be powerful incentives for waste recovery measures. In its ad, Reynolds Metal Company noted that 30 percent of the world's aluminum is reclaimed or secondary metal. A ton of aluminum can bring $100 from dealers, compared with $10 for steel and $16 for waste paper. To extend these momentary benefits to aluminum can drinkers and to ward off ban-type bills, the ad announced that Reynolds would pay a deposit for each aluminum can returned to company scrap dealers. Although this has triggered a rash of charitable collection drives, it remains to be seen whether this *ad hoc* approach to landscape litter will be sufficiently comprehensive.

Technological advances, increasing costs of conventional waste treatment, and improved environmental standards will all serve to expand the horizons of waste reuse and recycling. Waste reuse, however, will never achieve its true potential if tied strictly to the existing competitive market for compost, waste paper, cuttle (scrap glass), and aluminum can drives. The broad benefits of waste reuse make it preferable to conventional waste transfer techniques. Hart notes in his European composting study, "Composting is looked upon at Stuttgart [Germany] as a public service, not only to satisfy homeowner wants but also to demonstrate the principle of conservation. It is recognized and accepted by the city government that composting costs more than alternative waste disposal methods but that it is an appropriate community expenditure, the same as supporting city parks and museums." Waste reuse can not only reduce the pressures on the environment's waste-receiving capacity but on the environment's capacity for intensive exploitation. Materials reclamation can reduce the demand to mine the earth and fell the forests. Large-scale land fill and compost projects can redeem land tattered by picks and by steam shovels. Water reclamation can redeem underground aquifers and help reduce the need to erect dams, flood river valleys, and exhaust wilderness watersheds, and to otherwise meet water needs by mammoth interbasin transfers. Waste reuse thus tends to harmonize, rather than conflict, with the environment. While waste transfer is essentially anti-ecological, waste reuse is essentially ecological in nature.

These broad benefits constitute the traditional exclusions from waste management considerations. Political institutions will be challenged to integrate these considerations into economic and political policy. Local waste disposal agencies, with their fragmented vision, often have neither the resources or the motivation to exploit waste reuse strategies. Throwing wastes down the nearest river or hole will always appear cheaper and easier than blending together techniques of composting, compression, sanitary landfill, and salvage into a waste reuse strategy equipped to meet changing demands of wasteloads and materials markets. Intergovernmental funding and cooperation, as in Santee, are generally required to upgrade sanitary visions. (It is noteworthy that, whereas water supply and sewage treatment responsibilities are often divided between two separate local departments, the Santee Water District handled both responsibilities.) In funding local waste treatment projects, state and federal agencies could encourage and even require development of modern waste strategies that stress recycling rather then disposal, consolidated rather than fragmented management. Public agencies may find themselves judged by their success or lack of success in this regard. Stoyer, speaking before the 1967 International Conference on Water for Peace, concluded, "American voters have an admirable record of support for needed water development projects, but there is a danger of losing this support at some point in the future if we ask them to finance vast new works without showing them that we are making maximum use of what we have and that we make maximum use of proposed new supplies."

Although industry will undoubtedly utilize reuse concepts more as treatment costs mount, government agencies can adopt policies to encourage even broader waste reuse. Because of its dual potential in relieving water shortages and wasteload pressures, the Federal Water Quality Control Administration actively promotes expansion of water reclamation. "The ever-increasing volume and variety of waste discharges, combined with a rising demand for clean water, require the development of technology to permit more and more water reuse," notes one FWQCA report. Where incentives such as research and demonstration grants are not sufficient, regulatory methods should be considered to achieve modifications in product design that permit effective recovery. Consideration could also be given to a public policy of preferring secondary materials use over virgin materials use. Thus chemical fertilizers and soil conditioners could be restricted or prohibited in favor of compost fortified with residual waste nutrients.

Waste reuse can play an important role in environmental management, but it cannot be depended on to eliminate all other forms of waste control simply because it cannot redeem all wastes. There are wastes whose toxicity (radioactive and DDT residues), limited marketability (plastics), or sheer abundance (demolition debris, scrap wood, noise, silt, air emissions) are beyond waste recovery. Waste reduction and recovery technology becomes involved in a hectic race just to remain abreast of the spiraling rise in the national wasteload. "A remarkable feat was accomplished last year [1968] by this nation's auto wreckers," notes an Associated Press dispatch. "For the first time in memory they disposed of more vehicles than were abandoned, a score of something like 9 million to 7.5 million units." This sort of competition is too close for comfort, both for the natural and human environments. Another means of waste management becomes increasingly important: waste prevention.

SUGGESTED READINGS

WATER RECLAMATION

Ackerman, Edward, and George Löf, *Technology in American Water Development,* Baltimore: Johns Hopkins Press, 1959, chap. 16. Published for Resources for the Future.

American Institute of Chemical Engineers, *Water Reuse,* New York: American Institute of Chemical Engineers (345 E. 47th St., New York, N.Y. 10017), 1967. 39 papers on all facets of water reclamation by experts from around the world. Based on International Water Reuse Symposium in Detroit, 1967.

Bregman, J. I., "United States Research of Sewage Reclamation with Special Emphasis on Modern Sewage Treatment Approaches," address by FWQCA official to Israeli conference, February 24, 1969; available from FWQCA.

Culp, Russell, and Harlan Moyer, "Wastewater Reclamation and Export at South Tahoe," *Civil Engineering,* June, 1969. Mr. Culp manages the South Tahoe, Calif., treatment plant, considered the world's most advanced. Also author of *Advanced Wastewater Treatment,* New York: Reinhold, 1971.

Department of Health, Education, and Welfare, *Santee Recreation Project-Final Report,* Water Quality Control Research Series pub. no. WP-20-7, Washington, D.C.: U.S. Government Printing Office, 1967.

Kardos, Louis, "The Living Landscape Filter," *Landscape Architecture,* April, 1969.

Stoyer, Ray, "Development of 'Total Use' Management at Santee, California," presented at International Conference on Water for Peace, Washington, D.C., May 23–31, 1967, Santee, Calif.: Santee County Water District, 1967. See also "The Pressure Pipe Wastewater Treatment System," report prepared by Stoyer in 1969 for Irvine Ranch Water District, Irvine, Calif.

SANITARY LANDFILL AND COMPOSTING

American Public Works Association, *Municipal Refuse Disposal,* Chicago: Public Administration Service, 1966, chaps. 4 and 9.

Department of Health, Education, and Welfare, *Composting: European Activity and American Potential,* report by Samuel Hart, for Solid Wastes Program, no. 1826, 1968. See also *Summaries—Solid Waste Demonstration Grant Projects—1968,* Public Health Service pub. no. 1821, 1968; *Tezuka Refuse Compression System,* preliminary report prepared by American Public Works Association, 1969. HEW's Bureau of Solid Waste Management in Rockville, Md., has considerable additional material and reports.

Department of the Interior, *Surface Mining and Our Environment,* Washington, D.C.: U.S. Government Printing Office, 1967.

Los Angeles County Sanitation Districts, *Planned Refuse Disposal, See also* "Management of Solid Waste Disposal in Los Angeles County," address by Districts Manager John Parkhurst to Joint Committee of Governmental Agencies and Industry, August, 1968.

Metropolitan Sanitary District of Greater Chicago, "Land and Recreational Development Through a Rock and Solid Waste Disposal System," report prepared by Bauer Engineering, Inc., 1967. District also has information available on sludge farming and storm water reuse.

Shields, Wilfred, and G. Ward Barstow, "Use of Abandoned Strip Mines for Solid Waste Disposal in Maryland," *Progress Reports,* Baltimore: Maryland Department of Public Health, Division of Solid Wastes, 1966–1969.

MATERIALS RECLAMATION

American Public Works Association, *op. cit.,* chap. 10.

Bureau of Solid Waste Management, considerable material on subject of materials reclamation.

Darnay, Arsen, "Throwaway Packages—A Mixed Blessing," *Environmental Science and Technology,* April, 1969.

Landsberg, Hans, *op. cit.,* chaps. 4 and 5.

Wilson, David, "Technology and the Solid Waste Problem," *Technology Review,* February, 1969.

8
designed
for
coexistence

Few chemical compounds in the world can claim as many accolades in such a short period of time as DDT. Since its debut in World War II, this pesticide has been credited with saving agricultural economies, controlling diseases like malaria, and saving millions of lives. A Nobel Prize was awarded to its creator. Yet today the use of this "miracle" compound (as well as its chlorinated hydrocarbon cousins) is being banned or sharply restricted throughout the world.

DDT's downfall illustrates a rather dramatic application of waste prevention: the prohibition of any product or activity which defies effective and economical waste control. As John Evelyn's proposal to ban the new fuel, coal, from London indicated, this concept is by no means new. However, the idea that a product's impact on the environment should modify or determine its use has been regarded as an unwarranted and unneeded constraint on private industry and on a country's economic progress.

The realization that conventional waste treatment can no longer protect the environment from such an invitation to wholesale waste-making serves to legitimize waste prevention. Once released into the environment, DDT can affect nontarget as well as target organisms because of its broad-spectrum toxicity. Careful crop spraying with attention to meteorological conditions can reduce but not eliminate this threat. (Spraying by airplanes and ground rigs results in less than 10 percent of the pesticide reaching the target.) Once released, this broad-spectrum toxicity can be carried by water, in the air, or on a harvested crop to contaminate the globe. Even if subjected to some form of treatment during its global travels, such as a sewage treatment plant, it would emerge from the outfall relatively unscathed. DDT defies bacteria, either in nature or in sewage treatment plants. It decays slowly and is thus possessed of a relatively long life. This persistence is attractive to frugal farmers and a hazard to nontarget organisms. Its concentrations can thus build up in waterways and inside creatures to chronic and acute levels, as the brittle eggshells of the brown pelican suggest. This persistent, highly mobile, treatment-defiant broad-spectrum toxicity qualifies DDT as a waste emission out of control. DDT has already been banned in Sweden. Michigan, Arizona, and California have either banned or restricted its use and the federal government, through HEW, is now moving to eliminate DDT except for purposes deemed "essential" to health and welfare.

Waste prevention has been invoked in the case of uncontrollable emissions in warfare. The knowledge that gas attacks can easily backfire with a change in wind direction contributes to the international willingness to avoid gas warfare. Chemical and biological warfare (CBW), sometimes called "public health in reverse" is the target of an international movement to achieve agreement on its nonuse. The killing of 6000 grazing sheep by careless release of a CBW agent in Utah led to restrictions on CBW research in the United States.

The nuclear test ban treaty that bans underwater and above-ground nuclear tests stemmed from the dangers posed by radioactive fallout.

Wastes that are not particularly toxic can qualify for waste prevention because their nondegradable nature can defy or disrupt waste treatment processes. "Hard" detergents are biologically nondegradable. They continue to foam up, even in sewage treatment ponds,

designed for coexistence

tanks, outfalls, and rivers. This foaming action restricts a treatment facility's ability to handle degradable wastes. Hard detergents are slowly being phased out in favor of soft or degradable detergents. Because of similar manufacturing processes, however, both soft and hard detergents contribute to the phosphate load in our waters and resulting eutrophication. Entertainer Arthur Godfrey, an active conservationist, resisted doing commercials for a detergent manufacturer after learning of this factor. According to Godfrey, the manufacturer originally assured him the product was pollution-free, an assurance subsequently contradicted by FWQCA reports. Subsequently, Godfrey began the commercial by conceding its pollution impact.

Nondegradable litter items, such as throwaway cans and bottles, are becoming legislative candidates for waste bans, particularly in states who like their outdoors litter-free. Volunteer aluminum can collections have yet to prove their ability to control immortal litter.

Emission sources which can only be partially controlled can also become candidates for waste prevention. While stationary sources of air pollution are proving amendable to control measures, movable sources—particularly the auto—prevent a resolution of the problem. By 1980 the sheer increase in autos is expected to counter any reductions gained in emissions from the internal combustion engine. This specter is generating interest to ban the internal combustion engine and replace it with alternative power plants whose emissions do not obscure the sky. Some suggested alternative power plants are also being promoted for their ability to reduce another form of pollution, noise. Following his steam car trip, engineering professor William Gouse of Carnegie-Mellon University described the silence as "wonderful. You can ride along at 35 miles an hour hearing the birds."

Booms from supersonic airliners are presently beyond adequate technical control. As a result, the Department of Transportation plans to limit supersonic airline flights to the oceans. This sort of limitation is already generating concern among island nations, coastal yacht owners, commercial fishermen, and shipping lines. "As one who frequents coastal waters of the USA, I oppose using these waters as a dumping-ground for sonic booms from SSTs," begins a petition to President Nixon, submitted by the Citizens' League Against the Sonic Boom and signed by yachtsmen.

The threat of court-levied fines has been used to help prevent gross pollution discharges. If the fines are too small, however, this incentive for waste prevention is useless. California has upped its water pollution fines from a financial wrist-slap to a hefty $6000 per day. Canada is now considering legislation that would place pollution violations in the realm of criminal negligence, raising the possibility of jail sentences for offending city managers and corporation presidents.

Land-use planning can exploit the concept of waste prevention. Air emissions from an electrical generating power plant in Chicago could be much better controlled through extension of the smokestack. But the plant lies in the flight path to O'Hare International Airport and any extension would present a flight hazard. Positive examples of land planning to prevent or reduce pollution include compatible zoning around airports. Commercial and industrial development can be encouraged, and residential development—which has a much lower tolerance for jet noise—can be limited. This is hardly an economic restriction on land development. The presence of air transportation generates a considerable demand for commercial and industrial properties. Such compatible zoning might be coupled with buffer zones to separate residential or school receptors from hazardous noise levels.

Rezoning of an existing incompatible airport situation can be difficult. To permit far-sighted planning, Dallas's new airport site will embrace an 18,000-acre site. This size site will accommodate runways as well as compatible development. Miami and Dade County went into the Florida wilderness for a spacious site. Unfortunately, the site's proximity to the irreplaceable Everglades National Park raised serious water and noise pollution risks. As a consequence, the federal government withheld its approval of the proposed commercial jetport. The Miami experience suggests that there simply is not enough land

*designed
for
coexistence*

to make jumbo airport buffer zones the sole answer to airplane noise. The sight of 20 industrial firms lined up along an urban waterfront, although heartening to a Chamber of Commerce, is ecologically ludicrous. Industrial dispersion can make far better economic use of the natural waste-receiving capacity of the environment. Once more, land-use planning can exercise this form of waste prevention. Industrial development can be tailored to the receiving capacity of the region's airshed and watershed. With hindsight, it now seems unfortunate that so many chemical and oil refineries are located in a region with poor ventilating characteristics, the Los Angeles basin. The refineries now must pay a heavy price in air pollution control devices. Today the southern California coastal area is moving to prohibit any expansion or new construction of power plants because of their air emissions. Because of the uncontrollable nature of offshore oil spills, California is also seeking to prohibit offshore oil exploitation from certain geographic areas. The state's two senators are jointly sponsoring a bill to extend state offshore oil sanctuaries into federal waters. The fault-ridden geology of the area adds impetus to this form of waste prevention.

Waste prevention can also be realized through changes in industrial processes as well as products. Under a federal grant, a coal company in West Virginia is determining if men equipped with self-contained breathing apparatus can work efficiently in mines filled with nitrogen or some other inert gas. "If this new approach is successful," says Secretary of the Interior Walter Hickel, "we will be able to reduce lung diseases among coal miners, lessen the chances of explosions and fires in mines, and, at the same time, help prevent stream pollution by drainage of acids from both active and abandoned mines." Elimination of oxygen can curtail mine explosions and the natural reactions that cause acids to form in water draining from mines. In such waste prevention at the source lies the ultimate solution to siltation.

An interesting variant on waste prevention is to increase the assimilative capacity of the natural environment. Water from reservoirs can be released to augment low summer flow and waste assimilation in rivers. Investigations are also being conducted on the addition of oxygen to oxygen-depleted waterways.

Conventional waste treatment rarely presumes to dictate what products and activities society can indulge in, this is precisely why waste prevention can be so effective and yet so difficult to apply. Its application raises corollary issues: the economic and social ramifications of a ban and the availability of substitute products or services. Duck kills in marshes have been traced to ingestion of spent lead shot. Feeding birds who pick up the seed-like shot suffer paralyzed gizzards. Ammunition makers are now seeking to find a substitute for nonlethal pellets that will help to maintain duck populations and duck shoots. Market considerations rarely dovetail so nicely with goals of waste prevention. The willingness of many nations to forgo gas warfare and nuclear bomb testing undoubtedly stems from the availability of alternate means to wage war. In this light, the invention of gun powder and TNT might be considered godsends. Such handy alternatives to waste bans are usually not so readily or willingly available. Sometimes the cure can be as potentially hazardous as the disease. Power plants could significantly reduce their air emissions by switching from fossil fuels to nuclear power and raise the hazard of low-level and accidental radioactive emissions. Wholesale bans on offshore oil exploitation can increase dependence on oil tanker imports and the opportunity for oil tanker spills, which cannot be so readily traced as offshore oil well leaks.

The capability to produce or develop alternatives is often possessed by the very industry faced with a product ban. In this case traditional market considerations can clash profoundly with environmental considerations. Users and manufacturers of DDT strenuously opposed DDT bans. Automobile manufacturers presently oppose bans on the internal combustion engine. A DDT ban has been viewed as potentially harmful to farmers and to America's food and fiber supply for alleged lack of an effective substitute for pest control. A ban on the ICE *designed for coexistence* has been viewed as potentially disastrous for automotive transportation because of alleged lack of a feasible alternative. The product to be banned thus becomes as irreplaceable as the environment to be protected. A pro-DDT article in the business journal *Baron's* was headed, "Up with People and Down with the Venomous Foes of Chemical Pesticides."

In assessing these claims, government and the general public are faced with great difficulties. Generally the economic benefits of a particular product can be shown in very direct terms whereas the environment risks cannot be so readily reduced to economic terms. Traditionally there have been no government agencies to effectively assess, evaluate and balance economic and environmental considerations. Two government agencies, because of their particular responsibilities, can be at odds. The Department of Agriculture tended to emphasize the economic benefits of DDT while Interior and HEW were concerned about the environmental risks. Concerning the availability of alternatives, manufacturers are generally conceded to be the best judge of the industrial state of the art.

To resolve the DDT debate, many government study committees and commissions were appointed. This laborious *ad hoc* process resulted in the conclusion that DDT's environmental risks outweighed its alleged economic benefits. DDT's domestic market was actually declining, as pests were developing genetic resistance to it. Although not necessarily as efficient or well perfected as DDT, alternatives did exist in the form of biological pest control and low-persistent, narrow-spectrum pesticides. The economic convenience of DDT, certainly a market consideration, hardly justified the continued buildup of DDT levels in the environment. As the DDT debate illustrates, industry is not always the best judge of the infallibility of its products when environmental considerations are involved. Industry can still tend to view the environment as more adaptable than its products.

Government and university studies, as well as congressional investigations, now suggest that the internal combustion engine need not be the "eternal combustion engine." "Until recently I had thought of the steam car as one of those luxurious animals that had fallen by the wayside, a victim of the Darwinian laws of automotive selection," observed Congressman Richard Ottinger of New York. Continuing research on pollution-low power plants such as the steam engine, the gas turbine engine, and the electric engine now raise the possibility of effective alternatives to the ICE.

As alternatives emerge, the auto industry becomes very protective about its traditional prerogatives of product design and determination. The trade publication *Automotive Industries* editorialized, "When legislators, lawyers, prosecuting attorneys, lobbyists, and others who lack modern engineering training attempt to legislate engineering matters, they are moving into an area loaded with possibly much more hazard, risk, and danger for the public then they realize." However, Detroit's presumed monopoly of modern engineering training can appear directed more to the preservation of the ICE than to attainment of a pollution-free power plant. After one Ford official stated that his company was making the "maximum possible effort to overcome the [electric car's] present limitations," Henry Ford II told a *Look* reporter, "We have a tremendous investment in facilities for engines, transmissions, and axles, and I can't see throwing these away just because the electric car doesn't emit fumes." Before a Senate subcommittee, Ford official Herbert Misch testified, "We cannot overlook the fact that any power alternative, such as steam, must have sufficient merit to replace the internal combustion engine, which has benefited from the contributions of tens of thousands of engineers, scientists, and manufacturing experts over many years."

Misch's response caused Senator Edmund Muskie to pose a rhetorical question: "Doesn't all this, however, add to the momentum of the status quo in a way that may run counter to the public interest?" Later, in the same Senate hearing, a General Motors official, Dr. Lawrence Hafstad presented a performance comparison between steam engines and gasoline engines.

Senator Muskie: You characterize the emission index of the gasoline engine in 1970 as being low. This is the

designed
for
coexistence

same adjective you use for the steam engine. Actually, the performance of the steam engine would be several times better than the gasoline engine in 1970, will it not?

Dr. Hafstad: That is true.

Senator Muskie: You use the same adjective to describe widely differing performances in this respect.

Dr. Hafstad: This came about in trying to simplify the chart. I think we could say medium for the 1970, and we hope that the 1970–X would be low.

Senator Muskie: You ought to have low and lower, then.

Dr. Hafstad: That is right.

If proponents of the industrial status quo can be overly pessimistic about pollution-low alternatives, proponents of pollution-low alternatives can be overly optimistic. Millionaire industrialist William Lear attracted considerable public attention by investing in and promoting steam engine research. After investing his own money as well as federal research grants, however, Lear conceded that his research efforts showed the steam engine to be too complicated. As quoted by United Press International, Lear said, "I let them [air pollution officials] down. They thought the steam car was the answer to the pollution problem and I was the savior." Lear is now working to adapt steam engines to power trucks and buses, and gas turbine engines to the passenger auto.

Where a monopoly on industrial capability and innovation is not so concentrated, broader perspectives can emerge. In the vocabulary of the DDT and ICE defenders, a ban or restriction on nondegradable containers and throwaway bottles might be phrased as follows: "A threat to the entire packaging industry that endangers the nation's ability to transport liquids." Or "Should we ban throwaway cans just because they offend the senses of some wilderness lovers?" However, being broad-based and highly competitive, the container industry is beginning to absorb environmental considerations in a manner designed to strengthen product acceptability. Recognizing the litter quality of aluminum cans, the aluminum industry is stressing the potential for secondary recovery and sponsoring aluminum can collections. Glass recovery is not so economically enticing, although investigations are under way to use recovered glass as a road-building material. Glass firms are working to develop self-destruct containers: break-resistant bottles that shatter on hard blow into harmless granules or water-soluble glass protected by a coating during use which atmospheric moisture can disintegrate. Research is also under way on developing plastic beer containers that degrade in two years. Because so many containers wind up on road shoulders, degradable projects sometimes include provisions for fertilizing compounds in the residue. However, storm runoff could carry these fertilizers into lakes and add to algae growth problems. Work on water-soluble containers has also produced mixed feelings in one sector of waste management. The editor of *Water and Sewage Works* notes, "We are learning to cope with the kitchen waste disposal, cellulose cigarette filters, cigar tips, and disposable diapers. It is logical to assume that we could also learn to live with the residue of decomposed beer bottles."

As the container industry illustrates, expansion in materials and energy conversion that generates uncontrollable wasteloads can, by virtue of its diversity, be exploited to offer pollution-low alternatives. The public sector can utilize product bans, restrictions, and materials research to realize this potential. The Department of Agriculture is stepping up research on alternative pest control programs, including biological control, and HEW is sponsoring research on alternative power plant packages for automobiles. By ordering steam and natural gas demonstration vehicles, the public sector can also exploit its purchasing power in generating pollution-low alternatives. In land planning, public involvement in new town and urban renewal projects can serve to achieve industrial dispersion and integrated waste management. When waste prevention is joined with waste recycling, truly effective waste control becomes increasingly feasible. As Franklin Huddle observes in a congressional report, *Toward a National Materials Policy:*

I suggest as a conceptual goal the achievement of a nearly "closed" system in which materials retained

designed
for
coexistence

value throghout the system and were recycled rather than discarded. In this area, the pricing system needs to be supported, I think, by public investment in technological innovation, by public assistance in the employment of technologies to preserve and improve the environment, and by public regulation to compel reduction in the rate of specific degradations and to obstruct the introduction of new technologies that degrade the environment.

Such a closed system provides the public sector with the capability to transcend traditional political and economic constraints and protect our natural life-support system from our wastes. Such a prospective system also presents the public sector with the challenge to exercise increased control over the activities of a society in a fair and competent manner.

SUGGESTED READINGS

WASTE PREVENTION

Anthony, Harold, and George Fulton, "The Restoration of Natural Waterbodies," address before Operations Research Society Conference in June, 1969, on potential of oxygen addition to waterways by two engineers with the Denver, Colorado, division of Martin Marietta Corporation.

de Bach, Paul, ed., *Biological Control of Insects, Pests and Weeds,* New York: Reinhold, 1965.

McGrath, Dorn, "City Planning and Noise," address by HUD official before "Noise as a Public Health Hazard" Conference sponsored by HEW in February, 1969, and reprinted in *American Speech and Hearings Reports,* no. 4, 1969.

Senate Subcommittee on Air and Water Pollution, "Automobile Steam Engine and Other External Combustion Engines," joint hearings with Senate Committee on Public Works in 1968, Serial No. 90-82, Washington, D.C.: U.S. Government Printing Office. Considerable testimony and material on power plant alternatives and the economic ramifications of pollution-low alternatives in general.

Sweet, A. H., B. J. Steigerwald, and J. H. Ludwig, "The Need for a Pollution-Free Vehicle," *Air Pollution Control Association Journal,* February, 1968.

Worster, Charles, "DDT Stands Trial," *Aubudon,* September, 1969.

WASTE MANAGEMENT AS A CLOSED SYSTEM

National Academy of Sciences Committee on Resources and Man, *op. cit.,* Summary and Recommendations.

Senate Committee on Public Works, *Toward a National Materials Policy,* report prepared by representatives of the professional materials community, including Huddle, for this Senate Committee in 1969. Washington, D.C.: U.S. Government Printing Office, 1969.

9

power
with
control

If national security were conducted like waste management, the Army, the Navy, and the Air Force would be divided into state and local units, all of which would submit individual budgets based on their own particular estimate of local needs to 20 or 30 legislative committees. In reality the Army, the Navy, and the Air Force all exist within one department, the Defense Department, which formulates overall strategy, assigns priorities and submits a consolidated budget to Congress.

With our wastes threatening our national welfare, waste management also deserves high-level strategy making. Observes Cornell Professor R. H. Whittaker in an editorial in *Ecology:*

No one can predict what polluting substance or environmental alteration will first prove really damaging to human life, or whether these effects may become apparent in 1980, or in 2020. Such is the crux of the problem. It is almost certainly necessary that we change our ways of population growth and environmental alteration, but it is not possible to establish clearly the timing of the hazard, the degree of necessity, or the kind of strategy appropriate.

In Congress Senator Henry Jackson, who has traditionally concentrated on military affairs, observed:

In the last few years, it has become increasingly clear that, soon, some President and some Congress must face the inevitable task of deciding whether or not the objective of a quality environment for all Americans is a top-priority national goal which takes precedence over a number of other, often competing, objectives in natural resource management and the use of the environment. In my judgment, that inevitable time of decision is close upon us.

Within such a top-priority goal lies the opportunity to bring our waste emissions inside—not outside—schemes of control. Achievement of such a goal requires a comprehensive system for the assembly and reporting of environmental and waste knowledge and for the development of alternative actions. The Defense Department relies on university contracts and on specially created research institutions such as RAND and Aerospace for such a comprehensive system in national security. Professor Whittaker proposes creation of a National Institute of Ecology to foster ecological data banks, multidisciplinary field research, research coordination and advisory services for government and industry on action programs. Such broad-based research can begin to cope effectively with the diverse properties of waste emissions and the varying sensitivities of the environment. Research task forces can key on dangerous voids in knowledge, such as the implications of atmospheric turbidity from dust and carbon dioxide. Observes Dr. Haagen-Smit, "We'd better do something before we've either melted the polar ice caps and flooded the world's biggest cities, or before we have to suffer through an era of glaciation." Waste side-effects of new products or activities could be evaluated prior to release into the environment (and buildup of production investment). The pollution-low alternatives that our present state of materials and energy conversion could provide can be identified. The proper mix of public regulatory, research, and financial efforts in waste management can be investigated.

Such broad investigations can benefit from modern technology. Dr. Margaret Mead observed, before a House hearing, "Difficulties due to specialization are somewhat being resolved today by the fact that with computers it is possible to have a very rapid retrieval of information that crosses disciplinary barriers so you can have a high level of generalists and specialists working together with an adequate information control."

Some universities traditionally preoccupied with resource knowledge are beginning to meet the waste challenge. Some 30 midwestern universities and the Argonne National Laboratory are jointly studying the management of all wastes in Chicago's metropolitan area.

The Defense Department employs extensive intelligence and surveillance systems to apply limited resources on a priority basis. It has been suggested that a federal department, perhaps the Department of the Interior or a special commission, operate a surveillance system for the environment. Michael McCloskey, Sierra Club executive director, notes, "In performing its function of surveillance, there are certain problem patterns that it should especially look for: incompatibilities between programs; abrupt changes in trends or the pace of change; irreversible tendencies in trends; large accumulations of small incremental changes; stockpiling of trace elements; persistence of fugitive substances; random interaction of substances and forces in a reinforcing, or synergistic fashion; and the loss of unique and irreplaceable places and things." Such surveillance could uncover uncontrolled waste sources that jeopardize or counter waste control investments (see Tables 5 and 6).

Information and surveillance systems can be academic without effective application to policy-making. At the federal level, a department or council on environmental affairs has been urged, as well as a joint congressional committee on environmental quality. Such agencies could finally bring into focus a national strategy on the environment, including waste control. An Environmental Quality Council was established by President Nixon in 1969. Chaired by the President, the council consists of Cabinet members involved in environmental decisions.

The Citizen Advisory Committee on Recreation and Natural Beauty has been transformed into the Citizen Advisory Committee on Environmental Quality. The council aims to resolve environmental conflicts and promote environmental quality at the highest level. Two of the council's immediate concerns are with pesticides and air pollution. An early council meeting included a tour of autos with alternate power plants. The tour was preceded by a statement by the President's science advisor, Dr. Lee DuBridge, that the rise in automobile population could effectively counter emission reductions from present exhaust control system.

Considered a significant step forward, the President's Council has nevertheless been criticized for lacking the objectivity and the perspective that environmental and pollution problems require. Council members, including the Secretaries of the Interior, HEW, Transportation, and Agriculture, are all closely involved in making resource policies that can generate wasteloads and impair the environment. Once again the needs of the environment would be determined by prominent waste generators. Observed Senator Jackson, "The President really needs to be armed with information with which he can effectively deal with the Cabinet departments. He needs to be armed with impartial advice, even advice of an adversary nature which will place the options for decision before the President." In Senate testimony, former Interior Secretary Stewart Udall has posed the Council of Economic Advisers, appointed by and responsible only to the President, as a more suitable model.

The idea, of course—we were looking back over our shoulders at the depression—is that we wanted to set out as part of our national purpose that we were not going to tolerate serious depressions. We wanted to have full-employment economy. We wanted to have as a national goal that our economic system would function efficiently. And so we set up a council, and it has operated now for nearly 25 years . . . It has served to do much of the advance planning. It has monitored the week-by-week progress to see how the economy was functioning. And it seems to me the experience of

table 5

approaches to environmental health planning

	symptomatic approach	environmental systems approach	functional approach

Recognized Programs	Air pollution program
	Water pollution program
	Food sanitation program
	Occupational health program
	Radiological health program
		Health aspects of
		The urban environment
		The rural environment
		Occupational environment
		Recreational environment
		Transportation environment
		Domestic environment
		Educational environment
			Environmental monitoring
			  and surveillance
			Environmental quality
			  evaluation
			Environmental quality
			  protection

	Community noise Housing and health		
Evolving Programs	Drug abuse Motor vehicle accident prevention Home accident prevention Consumer health habits		

Source: Archives of Environmental Health, vol. 19, July, 1969. Devised by Dr. John Goldsmith.

table 6

classification of health department activities needed in a comprehensive environmental health program

program	environmental monitoring and surveillance	environmental quality evaluation	environmental quality protection
Air Sanitation, including[a] cigarette smoking, environmental respiratory diseases	Statewide cooperative air monitoring network; health surveillance; special studies	Air quality criteria and standards; motor vehicle standards	Motor vehicle pollution control and other control efforts
Food and drug, including[a] drug abuse	Food inspection; cannery and other facility inspection; drugs, cosmetics, hazardous household substances inspection; devices, medical nutritional quackery inspection	Food standards and tolerances; food processing standards; drug standards; hazardous substances evaluation; processing requirements	Labeling control; fraud prosecution; food processing licenses, food, drug, cosmetic adulteration, labeling and advertising
Housing	Environmental monitoring; epidemiological studies of housing, related illness, and accidents	Health standards; new housing; current housing standards	(No California State Department of Public Health Program)
Occupational health, including pesticides[a]	Special studies; noise monitoring; occupational environment surveillance; occupational health surveillance	Threshold limit values; safety standards; erogonomic standards	Prevention of occupational disease; diagnosis and treatment of occupational disease

Radiological health	User registration; air, water, food monitoring and surveillance; special studies; inspection of radiation facilities	Radiation health criteria; radiation machine standards; radioactive material standards	Licensing of isotopes; radiation machine control; radioactive material control
Water sanitation	Domestic water supply sampling; recreational water monitoring; shellfish surveillance; reclaimed water surveillance; special studies	Water supply standards; waste and reclaimed water standards; water related recreational standards; shellfish standards	Domestic water supplies and permits; waste treatment and reclamation preemptory orders; shellfish quarantine
Vector control, including solid waste management and rat control[a]	Vector surveillance; vector resistance surveillance (pesticides); arthropods (principally insects); small mammals (principally rodents)	Insecticide formulation and application standards; solid waste criteria	Zoonoses suppression; water-related vector control; field wilderness vector control; community area vector control; solid waste management control

[a] Programs included are new; the grouping with more established programs is based on similarities of technical staff requirements.

Source: *Archives of Environmental Health*, vol. 19, July, 1969. Devised by Dr. John Goldsmith.

this Council would indicate that if a Council on the Environment were to have similar encouragement and success, that it could function with equal effectiveness in terms of furthering national needs and national priorities.

In regard to the objectivity such an independent and expert body can offer, Senator Gaylord Nelson has offered the National Council on Drugs. "The Director of the Food and Drug Administration is able to stand on this independent body's recommendations. They are unassailable as a distinguished independent body. If it weren't for that and the FDA tried to do this alone, the drug companies would fold them up in 24 hours. That is what I am talking about, an agency which can't be folded up." Because of such congressional concern, President Nixon signed into law in 1970 a bill establishing an independent, three-man Council of Environmental Quality to recommend to the President national policies on the environment and carry out a continuing analysis of changes or trends in the environment.

A grand strategy or design for environmental protection would undoubtedly be defeated rather than advanced by the present fragmented system of waste control. At the same time, "nationalization" of this system may be both unwieldy and unnecessary. Consequently, proposals to upgrade the tactics as well as the strategy of waste control are being developed and tested. The Study Commission to Investigate Problems of Waste Pollution Control in Maryland proposes creation of a statewide Waste Acceptance Service. Rather than have several hundred independent sewer agencies control the use of state and federal water pollution control grants, the statewide service would own and operate all water treatment facilities. The service would accept all wastes; no direct discharges to waterways would be permitted. The service would be supported by charges based on the volume, toxicity, and strength of wastes received, this charge being an incentive for pre-treatment by dischargers. The "user" fee promises to become increasingly important in prorating and internalizing pollution control costs. The waste generator can judge whether it is more economical to treat and/or recycle his wastes or pay for this service. At the same time, the regulatory burden of the public control agency can be reduced. As economist Larry Ruff of the University of California at San Diego warns, "If we are not careful, the present pollution control programs, all based on direct control, will grow into powerful and inefficient bureaucracies, demanding more power as they become more ineffective." By relying on the use fee, contends Ruff, "The control authorities have a relatively simple job of measuring emissions and collecting fees, and do not make or enforce complex regulations or grant valuable favors." The use fee could be applied to solid wastes by placing a special tax on those nondegradable containers and products that burden solid waste disposal. While use fees and taxes have less applicability to air pollution control, steeply progressive taxes could be placed on high horsepower ICE engines to favor smaller, pollution-low motors.

The statewide scope of the proposed service would permit utilization of the full range of treatment technology and reuse. "The essence of the recommended program is that the state will manage its wastes rather than be managed by them," concludes the Study Commission.

In a waste management study for California, Aerojet-General Corporation recommended creation of waste management systems that would handle all forms of waste emissions, from air to solids to liquids. The Aerojet report notes, "The system collects waste, transports, processes and disposes of it, reclaims useful materials and takes into account the dilution and reaction of pollutants with the environment. The system is responsible for monitoring wastes as they are discharged into the environment and responsible for monitoring pollution levels of the environment." Meteorological and topographical conditions, such as frequency of temperature inversions and hydrologic regime, would define the boundaries of these waste systems. Thus management would be tailored to the waste-receiving capacity of the region, rather than arbitrary political lines. Such consolidated systems could avoid waste pollution transfer and plan for waste reuse and prevention. With a broad technical and economic base, such systems can realize the opportunity to expand treatment options, internalize control costs and make a national strategy for waste control a reality. The Aerojet report predicted that, by 1990, California would be spending $1.1 billion yearly for conventional waste control while incurring $7.4 billion in waste pollution damages. By upping this investment to $2.2 billion for improved technology and management, the report estimates that the pollution damage can be cut to $1.5 billion. Comprehensive waste management can thus be economical as well as effective.

At the federal level, a presidential proposal to consolidate pollution control agencies in the executive branch into an Environmental Protection Agency (EPA) was approved late 1970.

Such comprehensive management advances could have more than just domestic impact. "We are exporting insecticides and fertilizers to other countries and setting up in other countries technological problems that are giving them a great deal of trouble," Dr. Margaret Mead told a House hearing. "We have a kind of double responsibility not to export trouble and to have in mind designs that will also export our solutions in forms that can be used by other people rather than complicating their lives further." It is noteworthy that the federal crackdown on DDT does not extend to the largest market, foreign exports. Given the global travels of DDT residues, this loophole mocks our domestic restrictions and the efficiacy of our foreign aid. (James Wright, chief of the World Health Organization's vector biology and control section, opposes complete DDT bans in developing nations because no effective substitute to control malaria, dengue, sleeping sickness, and other insect-borne diseases has been identified by WHO. Wright claims that the volume of DDT used for health purposes is relatively small when compared with agricultural and forestry spraying.)

While such concepts as a national environment strategy, regional waste management, and user charges could solve critical waste control problems, these wide-ranging concepts raise other potential problems. As public health consultant Ron Linton, a vigorous proponent of such comprehensive concepts, observes, "When government seeks to apply its powers and resources toward major changes in industrial operations, in the affairs of state and local agencies and over the conduct and habits of private citizens, the processes of social and political action assume tremendous importance." The design of autos, the future of nuclear power, the location of new towns, the use of waterways, the merits of mass transit over auto transit, the practice of agriculture . . . these are just a sample of the activities that can and must be influenced as government becomes deeply involved in protecting us from our wastes. This deep involvement arouses traditional suspicions of centralized government and ponderous bureaucracy. Observed attorney Harold Green at an environmental conference, "Some means must be found, therefore, to assure that the setting of these *[environment safety]* standards, and the making of the cost-benefit judgments which underlie them, are the product of a broadly constituted body reflecting the interests and views of the general public and not merely of technical experts."

Concerns springs in part from a fear that such standards may stem from a strict preservationist determinism as narrow and self-defeating as economic determinism. This concern often stems from a misguided view of conservation and ecology. Microbiologist René Dubos in an article for UNESCO *Courier* observed, "Since man relates to his total environment and especially is shaped by it, conservation implies a quality of relationship rather than a static condition. Man must engage in a creative interplay with his fellows, animals, plants, and all the objects of nature that directly or indirectly affect him, and which he affects." There is perhaps a greater danger that waste management agencies may avoid the challenge of this creative interplay for a policy of creeping leniency. Too many regulatory commissions have become virtual captives of the very industry or activity they were established to regulate. Born of reform zeal, the Federal Trade Commission has become so lax in consumer protection that reform of the commission itself has become a major political problem. Membership in regulatory commissions often is synonymous with apprenticeship in political fund-raising or in the regulated industry. Commission hearings can be dominated by the testimony of industrial and private clients as reform elements relax their vigilance. Membership in the regional water quality boards in California is dominated by waste dischargers on the basis that they possess the most expertise in water quality matters. Broad public representation in appointive commissions on the environment can avert such built-in bias. Residents, educators, recreationists, sportsmen, college students, scientists, and conservationists have just as much at stake in our basic life support system as resource exploiters. Full and prompt disclosure of all information relating to environmental problems—coupled with extensive public hearings—can be another safeguard. Placing a proprietary stamp on information relating to wastes being emitted into air and water is not only dangerous but also oppressive. A joint congressional committee on the environment could be a powerful instrument of oversight. Congress cannot afford to accept executive decisions and programs on waste control with the same unquestioning acceptance traditionally accorded matters of national security. (Forebodingly, the same Congress that voted for the new independent Council on Environmental Quality failed to agree on one committee to receive the council's annual environmental report. As a result, the council's three members may have to testify before as many as 13 committees in the House and 11 committees in the Senate, all anxious to bask in the politically fashionable spotlight of environmental concern.)

In one respect, policy-making with an environmental perspective promises to be a liberating influence. A resident in a coastal community concerned by oil pollution may be referred to the Corps of Engineers, the Federal Water Quality Control Administration, the Coast Guard, the state conservation and tideland agencies, and the Public Health Service. All these agencies have responsibilities in oil pollution control; yet none has the continuing responsibility for coordinating these interests and making them intelligible to the public and its elected representatives. Broad-based waste agencies promise to inform rather than bewilder concerned citizens. Issues can be framed in the over-all public interest instead of single-mission responsibilities. Environmentalists can ob-

power with control   tain access to reliable and specific data. In supporting an independent Council on Environmental Quality, Yale ecologist F. Herbert Bormann observed:

Accurate data on local environment conditions supported by a respected national agency would do much to equilibrate the power of local conservationist groups vis-à-vis the bureaucratic and industrial forces. Such equilibration would produce better decisions at the local level and at the same time it would encourage all those who have the wish and the will to participate in the process of government to do so. It would help to dispose of the concept of individual impotence in the face of an immovable establishment.

This opportunity, of course, could be forefeited if environmental agencies couch waste pollution matters in "equilibration" and other precious buzz words so favored by aerospace engineers.

By countering the specialization of technical elitism, an environmental perspective cannot only bring our waste-making into line but enhance the system of democracy. "A national policy for the environment," observes political scientist Lynton Caldwell in a report for the Senate Interior Committee, "is one more step in the journey of the American people from political independence toward knowledgeable self-determination in its most fundamental and democratic sense."

SUGGESTED READINGS
WASTE MANAGEMENT AND PUBLIC POLICY

Department of Health, Education, and Welfare, *A Strategy for a Livable Environment,* 1967 report to the Secretary of Health, Education, and Welfare by Task Force on Environmental Health and Related Problems, chaired by Ronald Linton.

House Subcommittee on Fisheries and Wildlife Conservation, *Environmental Quality,* 1969 Hearings on a number of bills concerning a council on environmental quality, with testimony by Bormann, Mead, DuBridge, and many other representatives of varied institutions in society.

Murphy, Earl Finbar, *op. cit.*, chaps. 9 and 10.

National Academy of Sciences, *Waste Management and Control, op. cit.*, appendixes 6 and 7.

Ruff, Larry, "The Economic Common Sense of Pollution," *The Public Interest,* Spring, 1970.

Senate Committee on Interior and Insular Affairs, National Environmental Policy, 1969 Hearings with testimony by Senators Jackson and Nelson as well as Udall, McCloskey, Hickel, DuBridge, and Congressman Daddario. These hearings also include Lynton Caldwell's paper, "National Policy for the Environment."

Whittaker, R. H., "A View Toward a National Institute of Ecology," *Ecology,* Spring, 1969.

WASTE MANAGEMENT AS AN INTEGRATED SYSTEM

Aerojet-General Corporation, *op. cit.*, chaps. 4–9.

Dubos, René, "The Biosphere, a Delicate Balance Between Man and Nature," *UNESCO Courier,* January, 1969.

Kneese and Bower, *op. cit.*, chaps. 6–9, 14.

"Study Commission to Investigate Problems of Water Pollution Control in Maryland," *Journal of Sanitary Engineering,* April, 1968.

10
the
snow
is white
again

Once regarded as a smelly nuisance, wastes now threaten our entire environment and existence. The air we breathe, the water we drink, the lakes we swim in, the sounds we hear, and the landscape we see depend more and more on how we control wastes. We can no longer migrate from our wastes or only build longer outfalls and taller smokestacks. We must shape our style of materials and energy conversion to the needs of the environment as well as material comfort. The ability of the natural environment to assimilate wastes is as finite as our ability to process wasteloads.

In the nineteenth century, economists and natural historians predicted that the extractive capacity of the environment—its supply of raw materials—would limit our ambitions. That the supply of air and water would limit our mechanized horizons seemed absurd, so absurd that such substances rarely attracted the attention of economists, accountants, and public officials. Yet today, in the face of our massive wasteloads, the finiteness of the environment's assimilative capacity has been starkly revealed. We are running out of clean airsheds much faster than coal seams, food sources, and iron deposits.

Because waste-making is so deeply embedded in our way of life, effective waste control will depend less on technological "fixes" than on adapting our political and economic institutions to the waste challenge. To a society so adapted to "engineering" its way out of problems, this may be difficult to accept. But we will only bankrupt our budgets as well as our environment if we attempt to offset our present waste-making rate with more investment in conventional waste treatment. We can build a number of treatment plants on the Hudson River but never rescue it if effluent loads remain unchecked. We can continually refine auto exhaust systems but never clear the Los Angeles skies if internal combustion engines continue to multiply. Restraints on our present style of materials and energy conversion can only accomplish this.

As it stands, the cost of reclaiming the environment is going to be great enough. Although much of the waste pollution efforts have been directed at industrial activities, it must be stressed that the ultimate impact of all these efforts will fall on the individual consumer. Pollution control regulations may change industrial habits, but they do not assume the costs of change. Much of the cost will be passed on to us, the public, whether through taxes or costs of goods and services. The cost of living thus promises to grow over and beyond inflation effects. The cost of pollution control has already had a restructuring and redistributing effect on public and private money for other purposes, such as future space exploration. There are ominous signs that the cost required is not adequately recognized at the highest level of government. "I have become further convinced that the 1970s absolutely must be the years when America pays its debt to the past by reclaiming the purity of its air, waters and our living environment. It is literally now or never," proclaimed President Richard Nixon on January 1, 1970. The President thereupon promised to clean up water pollution in five years for $10 billion, of which $4 billion will come from federal funds. *The American City* editorialized in its March, 1970, issue:

If he is able to produce, he'll have to use some tricks that no one else knows. The best estimate that we have

*the
snow
is white
again*

had is that it will take $2.7 billion a year for 14 years to clean up the water pollution, based on 1966 dollars. It will take another $2 billion to upgrade the water facilities. President Nixon's $10 billion doesn't make a good start . . . And nobody has any idea how much it would cost to correct agricultural water pollution. As a matter of fact, nobody really knows how to go about it.

Waste pollution control, because of its cost, promises increasing controversy on a political level and for reasons other than just performance achieved. If certain sectors of our society, such as the troubled inner cities, feel that pollution control funds are "stealing" funds that could improve their social and economic lot—particularly educational and vocational funds—increased resistance to assuming these costs can be expected. If environmental cleanup becomes an intentional or unintentional means of postponing or delaying financing for other critical national priorities, the cause of pollution control as well as national harmony will suffer.

This situation will become exacerbated if inner-city residents feel they are paying not so much to clean up the air as for cleaning up after the mufflers of three-car suburban families who continually vote down bonds for expanded public transit. To achieve equity in pollution control, the costs must be placed on the producers and consumers of high-pollution activities, reaffirming once more the need to change the present uncontrolled style of materials and energy conversion. If increased fossil fuel consumption means increased offshore oil spills and blowouts, more polluted air, more thermal pollution, and more treatment costs, then fossil fuel consumption (and the activities it generates) must decrease, not expand. We are running out of environments that can be sacrificed to an ever-expanding economy of unlimited wasteloads. As Dr. David Gates, director of the Missouri Botanical Gardens, observed at an environmental symposium at Scripps Institute of Oceanography, we may be living in an age in which the material aquisitiveness of individual life has reached a zenith of affluence that can no longer be tolerated. The freedom to be wasteful, which is so central to affluence, has become the license to exterminate clean air and water. It is going to be cheaper and more equitable to adjust our material standard of living than to try to vainly keep abreast of wasteloads. Material comforts and convenience, as distinguished from necessities, must ultimately be priced out of the market if they are pollution-high. Fashionable obsolescence is one very ripe target in this respect. As *The American City* notes:

Why, incidentally, can't we persuade the automobile industry to drop its policy of yearly models so that a car won't be headed for the junk pile in five years primarily because of obsolescent style? The mechanical difference between a car built ten years ago and today is minor. More attention to longer service life would reduce the size of these graveyards and relieve this aggravating feature of land pollution.

In forgoing material comforts and convenience for a livable environment, we may find ourselves sorting garbage from metal and paper refuse to effect economic separation for materials reclamation. We may be storing and returning a multitude of containers, from milk bottles to wine bottles, to stem the tide of one-way litter items.

A switch from ornamental landscaping to native plantings could curb chemical fertilizer and irrigation runoff. We may even plant artificial lawns to obviate the initial need for fertilizers and water.

The ability to purchase a new car may be limited by the condition of the regional airshed. A limit of one car per family might bring biking, public transit, and hitchhiking back into public favor. (Many people would bike rather than drive an auto to the corner store if the roadways were safe. Newport Beach, California, for example, is planning a bikeway system along flood control channels and protected road shoulders to achieve this.) We may find mechanized recreation—from campers to "hogs"—banned from our national parks with transportation limited to foot, horse, or burro to ensure wilderness preservation over convenience. We may also find nonreturnable bottles and paper plates banned from our parks. During one holiday weekend in a desert park in California, talks by the naturalist ranger were temporarily cancelled. "I'm too busy trucking that stuff out," the naturalist explained, pointing to a garbage pickup station overflowing with camping refuse. Needless to say, this added duty does little for ranger morale.

The realization that we can live without much of the physical waste that affluence breeds may be one of the great values of environmental cleanup. Many people, particularly youths, are already following these precepts and finding them not unduly burdensome and often quite economical. Unhitched from an internal combustion engine in a wilderness, a person is that much less estranged from the sights, sounds, and natural delights of this planet. With less slavish reliance on the latest labor-saving device, one can achieve a more rewarding sense of physical and material self-sufficiency. Some families who have always lived in an urban environment are discovering the pleasure of growing fruits and vegetables in their backyards with the aid of compost from their garbage. Although the economic gains may be only minor, the social satisfaction is not.

At a community or national level, materials and water reclamation, by contributing to resource self-sufficiency, can reduce dependence on resource imports with its complicated and sometimes injurious political and social overtones. Too often the United States has recruited the resources of an undeveloped nation only to wind up with a resentful economic colony. *The American City* observes, "Why, we can ask the steel industry, does it continue to go to South America or some similar remote spot and dig iron ore out of a hill when we have plenty of ferrous metal perched on hillsides throughout the nation available for their use? We call them automobile graveyards."

Comprehensive waste management promises to contribute to foreign relations in a far different manner than obsessive virgin materials recovery. It will do little good for the United States or other nations to invest heavily in pollution control if their efforts are countered by careless radiation leaks and offshore oil spills from neighboring nations. The realization that waste management must be international in scope has helped to foster a United Nations Conference on the Environment in 1972. In an article in the Los Angeles *Times* of December 28, 1969, reporter Earl Foell envisions pollution "sleuths" available to track down international pollution sources. The case for spot environmental monitoring of the open ocean for oil spills is already a strong one. Such pooling of pollution control efforts could help deter developing nations from falling into the wasteful habits of older industrial nations. By going directly into advanced sewage treatment, a developing nation can conserve on water needs and avoid river cleanups. What technology we develop for materials reclamation will be doubly beneficial to a nation with a shortage of resources to begin with.

Such restraints on physical waste thus promise to have beneficial social fallout, but the main goal of comprehensive waste management remains a healthy and clean environment. This goal requires that our airsheds, waterways, eardrums, and land no longer be used as cheap dumps to absorb wasteloads out of control. Delay and indecisiveness hastens emergence of an increasingly hostile environment. Our major rivers become heavily polluted over the last 50 years, our urban airsheds the last 30 years. "We are looking down the barrel of a high-caliber problem that gets tougher by the day: finding the proper fit for an increasing number of ecological interfaces," observes H. B. Hickey of Resources Research. The barrel now holds a new bullet—light emissions. Go-Go girls who work under psychedelic lights are the subject of HEW studies on possible eye damage from ultraviolet emissions. The TV industry has called back color TV models which emit radiation in excess of recommended levels. Laser emissions can burn holes in the retina of the human eye as well as scar skin tissues. A Laser Safety Conference sponsored by the Public Health Service in 1968 reported, "With the continued progress of laser technology, consideration should be given to consumer protection from laser devices which may be used in open operations, such as pipe laying, surveying, laser radar systems, for aircraft, vehicles of locomotion, such as autos, trucks and trains, for laser radar canes for the blind, laser applications in home television systems, and advertising displays."

As usual, concern for safe ecological interfaces is

hardly keeping pace with exploitation. In setting out to register laser devices, the Illinois Department of Public Health assumed 25 to 40 such devices might exist in the state. Yet the engineering department of one university was found to have 500 small lasers emitting low-level radiation. This casual laser dispersion suggested to the Illinois officials the need for safety programs, including warning signs. Unfortunately, there was one hitch. "Obtaining personnel with training in laser safety is virtually impossible," noted the departmental report. The 1968 report concluded, "We have no means of predicting the magnitude of the laser problem in Illinois at this time."

Our habitat technology permits us to survive in space, on the moon, on the seabed, and in other hostile environments. Undoubtedly our technology, up to a point, could prolong survival on a planet rendered hostile by our careless waste emissions. Man, like the rat, the cockroach, and the urban monkeys of India, is a relatively adaptable creature and could probably adapt to wearing a stylish gas mask, earplugs, and sulfur-resistant clothes on periodic forays from geodesic life habitats serviced by synthetic water, sights, and sounds. Yet it would be ironic if the threat from our wastes would realize the sterile social specters of *1984* and *Brave New World.* Comprehensive waste management gives us a more wholesome choice: the chance to live outdoors as well as exploit its resources. The air is clear and the snow white again in London because John Evelyn's advice in 1661 —sharp restrictions on coal burning—is finally being heeded.

We could, of course, adopt the most progressive waste control programs and still not be safe from pollution in a world where population levels are not controlled. The waste management system that can handle an infinite number of people is not and never will be developed unless periodic plague is promoted. In fact, waste-control related disasters in technologically advanced countries —such as acute air pollution—may become as severe a health threat as food shortages in developing nations. We cannot afford to outgrow our planet until—if ever— we can colonize the universe. It is probably fitting that our colonizing ability will depend in part on our ability to protect the universe from waste contamination. The fact that spent space hardware orbiting aimlessly in space is already considered a navigational hazard is a questionable omen. Tons of spent space fuel discarded on the moon may have a high catalytic potential from high-energy particles in the solar winds. If the history of our waste-making tells us anything, we can learn that releasing wastes in a spirit of innocence is a good guarantee of a debilitated environment and an imperiled *Homo sapiens.*

SUGGESTED READINGS

COMPREHENSIVE

Commoner, Barry, *Science and Survival,* New York: Viking, 1966.

De Bell, Garrett, ed., *The Environmental Handbook,* pts. I and II ("Eco-Tactics"), New York: Ballantine, 1970.

Dubos, René, *So Human an Animal,* New York: Scribners, 1968.

Goldsmith, John, "Managing Man's Habitat," *Archives of Environmental Health,* July, 1969.

Leopold, Aldo, *A Sand County Almanac,* New York: Oxford, 1949.

McHarg, Ian, *Design with Nature,* New York: Natural History Press, 1969.

LASERS

First and Second International Laser Safety Conferences and Workshops, *Archives of Environmental Health,* March, 1969; February, 1970.

index